"ADVICE TO A YOUN
AND OTHER :

BY SIR JOHN FLOYER MD (1649-1734) OF LICH
IN STAFFORDSHIRE

The 18th-century views of Lichfield on the covers are from an engraving, *The South West Prospect of the City of Lichfield* (1732), by the brothers Samuel and Nathaniel Buck, photographed by Richard Lewington of Appleford, Oxon.

Fig. 1. *Sketch of Sir John Floyer* (Bodleian Library, G.A. Staffs 4°8).

"Advice to a Young Physician" and Other Essays

by Sir John Floyer MD (1649-1734)
of Lichfield in Staffordshire

Introduced and Edited by
Denis Gibbs and Philip K. Wilson

William Sessions Limited
York, England

Denis Gibbs and Philip K. Wilson 2007

ISBN 978-1-85072-363-9

Printed in Plantin Typeface
from the Editors' Disk
by Sessions of York
The Ebor Press
York, England

Contents

Preface

THIS COLLABORATIVE venture was initially planned following the lecture one of us (DDG) gave in October 2002 entitled, "Continuities and Changes: A Young Student of Physick Three Centuries Ago". This lecture, the inaugural presentation in the Hershey Lectureship in the History of Medicine at Penn State University's College of Medicine and Milton S. Hershey Medical Center in Hershey, Pennsylvania, USA, was chiefly sponsored through the generous benefaction of Dr Graham Jeffries, with additional support of the College's Department of Humanities and its Chairman, Professor J.O. Ballard, and the Drs Kienle Center for Humanistic Medicine under its Director, Professor David Hufford. The other editor (PKW) received a fellowship to participate in the Sir John Templeton Oxford Seminars on Science and Christianity held over three consecutive summers (2003-2005) at Wycliffe Hall, Oxford. This opportunity allowed the editors to work more closely together during part of each of these summers. A sabbatical leave approved by Penn State University's College of Medicine brought PKW to Lichfield, England to finish this joint venture in Autumn 2006.

The Provost, Fellows and Scholars of The Queen's College, Oxford, generously allowed us access to books and manuscripts in the College library, with permission to publish material from the Floyer Collection, as well as several accompanying illustrations. It is a special pleasure to record the invaluable help of Amanda Saville and her staff in the College library. Mary Clapinson, formerly Keeper of Special Collections and Western Manuscripts in the Bodleian Library, offered expert advice on the manuscripts while she was preparing her *Catalogue of the Manuscripts of Sir John Floyer, The Queen's College, University of Oxford*. One of us (DDG) first enquired about the Floyer manuscripts nearly forty years ago. On occasional visits over the years, successive librarians including the late Robin Drummond-Hay, Helen Powell and Jonathan Bengston have been most welcoming and encouraging. While investigating the provenance of books in the Floyer collection, Helen Powell added a new dimension to studies on Floyer by making the important discovery that many of the earliest books in the collection had previously belonged to Dr Anthony Hewett, Floyer's predecessor in Lichfield. PKW is grateful for the hospitality extended to him by The Queen's College as an Additional Member of the Common Room. As a Templeton Fellow in Oxford, PKW had the privilege of working in the Bodleian Library, as well as the opportunity for annual discussions with Ronald Milne, former Acting Director of University Library Services and Bodley's Librarian, on the subject of Floyer.

The editors are grateful to the many individuals who offered their assistance and support throughout this project. Professor Janet Davis of Truman State University, Kirksville, Missouri, USA, reviewed and revised our translations of the Greek passages in the manuscripts. Christopher Purvis, as an undergraduate reading Greats at Oxford in 1972, kindly provided the first expert translations of Floyer's Latin and Geek into English. Robert Curley, the Senior Editor for Science at Encyclopaedia Britannica, Inc., provided helpful source verification. Over the years, one of us (DDG) has particularly appreciated the help of staff in the Lichfield Record Office, the Staffordshire Record Office and the William Salt Library in Stafford, and in the Samuel Johnson Birthplace Museum in Lichfield. Douglas Johnson, formerly an assistant editor of the *Victoria County History of Staffordshire* has, on many occasions, provided new insights concerning members of the Floyer family of Hints. We are also grateful for the help of Pat Bancroft of the Cathedral Library in Lichfield.

There are many friends among medical historians and librarians in London who have been generous with their time and always happy to share their learning; Harold J. Cook, Director of the Wellcome Trust Centre for the History of Medicine at University College London and John Symons, recently retired from the post of Curator of Early Printed Books at the Wellcome Library for the Understanding of Medicine, have been especially helpful. The interest and encouragement of John Wiltshire of the English Department, La Trobe University, Melbourne, Australia, author of *Samuel Johnson in the Medical World: The Doctor and The Patient* (Cambridge: Cambridge University Press, 1991), have always been appreciated.

Illustrations have been selected with the dual purpose of complementing the text of "Advice to a Young Physician" and of providing small glimpses of the contemporary scene in which Sir John Floyer lived and practised. Both the sketch of Sir John Floyer shown in the frontispiece and that of Floyer's Cold Bath at Abnalls near Lichfield, are reproduced by kind permission of the Keeper of Western Manuscripts, Bodleian Library, Oxford. The photographs of the Physician's Pulse-Watch made by Samuel Watson were generously provided by the late Mr T.P. Camerer Cuss. His son, Mr T.A. Camerer Cuss, also a distinguished horologist, kindly gave permission for their publication. One of us (DDG) is especially indebted to Pat Burgess, formerly of the Photographic Department of the Royal London Hospital, who skillfully photographed many illustrations from books in the editor's personal collection.

The project would not have progressed as it did without the steadfast encouragement and support of our respective wives, Rachel Gibbs and Janice Wilson. Rachel challenged our thinking on several occasions in ways that improved the presentation of our project. Janice offered her skill as a librarian in guiding the compilation of the glossary and the index, as well as verifying the accuracy of our transcription of the entire manuscript. In our transcription of the manuscript, the original spelling has usually been retained, whereas the punctuation has often been modified.

DDG & PKW

List of Illustrations

Selective Chronology
Sir John Floyer (1649-1734)

1601   **Ralph Floyer, father of Richard Floyer and grandfather of John Floyer bought property at Hints, Staffordshire**
1602   Bodleian Library opened
1603   **Richard Floyer, father of John Floyer born**
1611   King James Bible; authorised version
1617   Anthony Hewett, physician in Lichfield preceding John Floyer, matriculated Christ's College, Cambridge
        Elias Ashmole, antiquary, Windsor Herald, and founder of Ashmolean Museum, b. Lichfield (d. 1692)
        Society of Apothecaries founded
1618   *London Pharmacopoeia* issued by College of Physicians
1621   Oxford Botanic Garden founded by Lord Danby
        Thomas Willis, influential physician and teacher in Oxford and London, b. Great Bedwyn, Wiltshire (d. 1675)
        Jacob Bobart b., Keeper of Oxford Physic Garden from 1642 (d. 1680)
1624   Thomas Sydenham, the "English Hippocrates", b. Wynford Eagle, Dorset. (d. 1689)
1627   Robert Boyle b. (d.1691)
        John Ray b. Black Notley, Essex (d. 1705)
1628   Marcello Malpighi b. (d. 1694)
        William Harvey: *De Motu Cordis*
1632   John Locke b. Somerset (d. 1704)
        Antoni van Leeuwenhoek b. Delft, Holland
1634   Robert Hooke b. Isle of Wight (d. 1703)
        Francis Willughby b. Middleton Hall, Warwickshire (d. 1672)
1635   Samuel Watson, watch & clockmaker, b. Coventry (d. *c*1712)
1636   Anthony Hewett: MD Padua. (Incorporated MD Cantab. 1637)
        Phineas Fowke of Little Wyrley Hall, Staffordshire, b. Yorkshire (d. 1710)
        Sanctorius d. (b. 1561)

1638 John Tradescant the Younger inherited family property at Lambeth on the death of his father and became Keeper of His Majesty's Gardens, Vines and Silkworms
Countess of Chinchon cured of malaria by Peruvian bark

1640 Edward Baynard, b. Preston, Lancashire, physician in London and Bath, joined **John Floyer** in authorship of *History of Cold Bathing* (1702) (d. 1721)

1642 22 Aug. First Civil War started; Oxford a Royalist centre
Thomas Sydenham matriculated but left Oxford to join Dorset Militia
Isaac Newton b. (d. 1729)

1643 2-5 March, First Siege of Lichfield – a Royalist stronghold; Lord Brooke's Parliamentarian army entered Lichfield and the Royalists retreated into The Close from where they eventually surrendered
8-21 April, Second Siege of Lichfield; Royalist Prince Rupert surrounded The Close and led a victorious attack on the Parliamentarians within

1644 John Milton: *Of Education*

1645 **Richard Floyer m. Elizabeth daughter of Zachary Babington of Curborough, near Lichfield**

1646 9 March-10 July, Third Siege of Lichfield; ultimate Royalist defeat
24 June Oxford, Charles I's capital city, surrendered to Parliament forces
Thomas Sydenham returned to Oxford and began studying medicine
Mathew Floyer, elder brother of John Floyer, b. Hints

1647 **Mary Floyer b. Hints**
William Gibbons b. Wolverhampton, London physician, friend of John Floyer (d. 1728)
John Wilkins b. 1614, warden of Wadham College (1647-1659) (d. 1672)

1648 William Petty: *The Advice of W[illiam]P[etty] to Mr Samuel Hartlib for the Advancement of Some Particular Parts of Learning*
Philosophical Society (Clubbe) of Oxford formed

1649 30 January. Execution of King Charles I. Proclamation of Commonwealth
3 March. **John Floyer b. Hints Hall, Staffordshire**

1650 Anne Green revived in Oxford by Thomas Willis and William Petty, Reader in Anatomy, after judicial hanging
Samuel Floyer b. Hints

1651 William Harvey: *De Generatione Animalium*
John Hough b. (d. 1743)

1652	John Radcliffe b. in Wakefield, Yorkshire, in December 1652 or in January 1653
	John Locke student of Christ Church Oxford (until 1656)
	True Floyer b. Hints
1653	**Peter & Prudence Floyer (twins) b. Hints**
	Hooke entered Christ Church Oxford
1654	Boyle resident in Oxford (until 1688)
	John Bellers b. (d. 1725)
1656	Michael Johnson, father of Samuel Johnson, b. Derbyshire (d. 1730)
1657	Simon, 4th Baron Digby of Geashill b.: lived at Coleshill Hall, Warwickshire. (d.1685)
	Accademia del Cimento founded in Florence
	Hooke: balance spring
1658	Jan Swammerdam observed red blood corpuscles
1659	George Antrobus, Headmaster of Tamworth Grammar School, b. (d. 1708)
	Forerunners of Royal Society met in Boyle's lodgings
	Boyle started experiments with air-pump
1660	Charles II restored to the throne; Episcopy re-established
	John Ray: *Catalogus Plantarum circa Cantabrigiam Nascentium*
	William, 5th Baron Digby b. (d.1752)
1661	Georg Ernst Stahl ran the first course in chymistry at Oxford
	John Hacket appointed Bishop of Lichfield & Coventry (d. 1670)
	Malpighi observed capillary circulation in frog's lung
	Boyle: *Sceptical Chymist*
1662	Boyle discovers law relating to the pressure and volume of a gas
	Christopher Wren designed Sheldonian Theatre
	Hooke designed compound microscope
1663	Royal Society incorporated by Royal Charter (Charles II)
1664	**John Floyer: matriculated, commoner, The Queen's College, Oxford**
	Thomas Willis: *Cerebre Anatome*
1665	23 March. John Radcliffe matriculated at University College, Oxford, at age 13
	June-Dec. The Great Plague in London
	Court of Charles II and Parliament in Oxford (Sept. 1665-Jan. 1666), on account of the Great Plague
	Boyle & Hooke conducted "philosophical experiments" in Deep Hall, High Street, Oxford
1666	Hooke: *Micrographia*
	Philosophical Transactions starts publication
1667	**John Floyer: BA Oxon.**
	Willis, Lower and Locke left Oxford for London

1668 Herman Boerhaave b. (d. 1738)
Boyle left Oxford for London
1669 Robert Morison, Professor of Botany at Oxford
Francis Willughby invited John Ray to work at Middleton Hall, near Tamworth (until 1675)
1670 28 Oct. Bishop John Hacket d. in Lichfield
Jacob Bobart the Younger, Keeper of the Oxford Physic Garden & Professor of Botany
1671 **John Floyer: MA Oxon.**
George Cheyne b. (d. 1743)
1674 Thomas Willis: *Phamaceuticae Rationalis*, Willis d.1675
1675 **John Floyer living in Tamworth Street, Lichfield**
1676 John Ray living in Sutton Coldfield (1676-70)
1677 Robert Plot, antiquary and county historian published *Natural History of Oxford-shire* (d. 1696)
Leeuwenhoek observed spematozoa
1679 January: **Elizabeth Floyer, mother of John Floyer, d. aet. 61**
August: **Richard Floyer, father of John Floyer, d. aet. 77**
1680 Apr. **John Floyer m. Mary Fleetwood (née Archbold), widow of Arthur Fleetwood**
John Floyer: Doctor of Medicine, Oxon.
1681 **John Floyer (John II), son of John & Mary Floyer, b. Lichfield**
1682 John Ray: *Methodus Plantarum*
Andreas Cleyer, physician and botanist, published *Specimen Medicinae Sinicae*, a work on Chinese medicine
1683 **Archbold Floyer, second son of John & Mary Floyer, b. Lichfield**
Ashmolean Museum, Oxford, opened to the public and Plot, Prof. of Chymistry, appointed its first Keeper; Oxford Philosophical Society reorganized
1684 January: **John Floyer knighted by King Charles II**
Anthony Hewett MD, Lichfield physician, d.
Boyle: *Mineral Waters*
Plot: *De Origine Fontium*
1685 King Charles II d. Accession of King James II
1686 **Sir John Floyer elected a member of the Philosophical Society of Oxford**
Plot: *Natural History of Stafford-shire*
Ray: *Historia Plantarum*, Volume I (Vol. II, 1688)
1687 **Sir John Floyer:** Φαρμακο-βαςανος*; or, The Touch-stone of Medicines, Discovering the Virtues of Vegetables, Minerals and Animals, by their Tastes and Smells*, Volume I Published by Michael Johnson

Bishop's Palace rebuilt in the Cathedral Close, Lichfield, after long delays

1689 James II superceded by William and Mary

1690 **Sir John Floyer: *The Touchstone of Medicines*, Volume II**
Locke: *Essay on Human Understanding*
Phineas Fowke inherited Little Wyrley Hall
Samuel Watson left Coventry for London

1692 Building of the new library, The Queen's College, Oxford started (Completed in 1695)
Ray: *The Wisdom of God Manifested in the Works of the Creation*

1694 Ray: *Three Physico-theological Discourses*
Philip Dormer Stanhope, 4th Earl of Chesterfield b.

1695 A census of the population of Lichfield carried out by Gregory King (1648-1712)

1696 **Sir John Floyer: *The Preternatural State of the Animal Humours, Described by their Sensible Qualities, which Depend on the Different Degrees of their Fermentation. And the Cure of each Particular Cacochymia is Performed by Medicines of a Peculiar Specific Taste, Described***
Published by Michael Johnson
Dispensary set up by the College of Physicians in Warwick Lane

1697 **Sir John Floyer**: *An Enquiry into the Right Use of and Abuses of the Hot, Cold, and Temperate Baths of England* (Abbreviated Latin editions, 1699, 1718)

1698 **Sir John Floyer: *A Treatise of the Asthma*** (Subsequent editions, 1717, 1726, 1745; French editions 1761, 1771, 1785; and German edition 1782)

1699 **Sir John Floyer**: *Philosophical Transactions* contribution, "A Relation of Two Monstrous Pigs with the Resemblance of Human Faces, and Two Young Turkeys Joined by the Breast"
John Hough appointed Bishop of Lichfield (until 1717)

1702 **Sir John Floyer: *The Ancient ΨΥΧΡΟΛΥΣΙΑ Revived; or, An Essay to Prove Cold Bathing both Safe and Useful*** (Subsequent editions 1706, 1709, 1715, 1722, 1732; Abbreviated edition, 1844; German editions 1749, 1832, 1852)
Sir John Floyer: *Philosophical Transactions* contribution, "Observations on the Class of Sweet Tastes, Made by Comparing the Tastes of Sweet Plants with Monsieur L'Emery's Chymical Analysis of Them, in his *Treatise of Drugs*"
King William III d., Accession of Queen Anne

1706 **Sir John Floyer m. Margaret Whitehall, Lichfield Cathedral**

1707 **Sir John Floyer: *The Physicians Pulse-Watch; or, An Essay to Explain the Old Art of Feeling the Pulse, and to Improve*** *it by the Help of a Pulse-Watch*, Volume I (Italian edition, 1715; Subsequent English edition 1988)

1709   Samuel Johnson b. Lichfield

1710   **Sir John Floyer:** *The Physician's Pulse Watch; or, An Essay to Discover the Causes of Diseases and a Rational Method of Curing Them by Feeling the Pulse*, Volume II

1712   Samuel Johnson taken by his mother, on the recommendation of Sir John Floyer, to Westminster Abbey and touched for the King's Evil by Queen Anne

        Sir John Floyer: *Sibylline Oracles Translated from the Best Greek Copies, and Compar'd with the Sacred Prophesies, Especially with Daniel and the Revelations, and with so much History as Plainly Shews, that Many of the Sibyls Predictions are Exactly Fulfill'd. With Answers to the Objections Usually made Against Them*

1714   John Bellers*: An Essay Towards the Improvement of Physick*

        Herman Boerhaave succeeded Govard Bidloo as Professor Collegei Medico-practici (Leiden)

        Queen Anne d. Accession George I

1715   **Sir John Floyer:** *A Vindication of the Sibylline Oracles*

1716   13 Sept. **John Floyer (III), grandson of Sir John Floyer, baptised Penkridge Church, Staffordshire**

1717   3 Dec. **Susannah Floyer, grand-daughter of Sir John Floyer bap. Longdon, near Lichfield**

        Sir John Floyer: *Two Essays. The First Essay Concerning the Creation, Aetherial Bodies, and Offices of Good and Bad Angels. The Second Essay Concerning the Mosaic System of the World. Which being Explain'd, is Preferable to All Other Systems*

        Samuel Johnson entered Lichfield Grammar School.

        Lady Mary Wortley Montagu introduced inoculation (variolation) against smallpox, from Turkey

1719   **Sir John Floyer:** *An Exposition of the Revelations, by Shewing the Agreement of the Prophetic Symbols with the History of the Roman, Saracen, and Ottoman Empires and of the Popedom*

1720   12 Dec. **John Floyer (III), grandson of Sir John Floyer, d. buried Lichfield Cathedral**

1721   **Sir John Floyer:** *The Prophecies of the Second Book of Esdras Amongst the Apocrypha, Explained and Vindicated from the Objections made Against Them. To which are added: A Comment on the Prophecies of Zachary and Micah: With Some Observations Concerning the Prophecies of Daniel and Malachi. Likewise the State* *of the Jews After the Return of the Two Tribes, till the Resurrection of the Just. As also a Description of the State of the Israelites of the Ten Tribes, after their Return into their Countrey*

1722   Sir Hans Sloane, President of the Royal College of Physicians, President of the Royal Society, presented his garden in Chelsea to the Society of Apothecaries

        Sir John Floyer: *An Essay to Restore the Dipping of Infants in their Baptism, with a Dialogue Betwixt Curate and his Parishioner, Concerning the Manner of Immersion*

        Sir John Floyer: *A Letter to the Right Honourable Mr C[harles] S[tanhope] Concerning the Inoculation of the Small Pox*

1724   Sir John Floyer: *Medicina Gerocomica; or, The Galenic Art of Preserving Old Men's Healths* (Subsequent editions, 1725, 1738, 1979)

        Sir John Floyer donated books together with his unpublished manuscripts to The Library, The Queen's College, Oxford

        Sir John Floyer: *Letter to the Honourable Mr C[harles] S[tanhope] Concerning the Regimen of Health of the Younger Years and Adults, as Galen has Observed them*

1726   Sir John Floyer: *A Comment on Forty-Two Histories Described by Hippocrates in the First and Third Books of the Epidemics*

1727   George I d. Accession of George II

1728   Letter from **Sir John Floyer** to Mr King of Bungay in Suffolk, recommending cold baths

1729   1 April. **Dame Margaret Floyer died**

1730   Michael Johnson d. in Lichfield

1731   Erasmus Darwin, physician in Lichfield 1756-1781, b. Chesterfield

1734   31 Jan. **Sir John Floyer d. in Lichfield, buried in the Cathedral burial ground; no memorial survives**

Introduction

Biographical Sketch

FOR OVER HALF a century, Sir John Floyer (1649-1734) (Fig. 1) practised as the only physician in the small cathedral city of Lichfield in the English midlands.[1] He had been born and brought up in the manor house in the small village of Hints, situated between Lichfield and Tamworth in southeast Staffordshire. He died in Lichfield when he was nearly 85, in 1734. His family were staunch loyalists. Floyer was born in the year that King Charles I was executed, was a young boy during the Interregnum, was eleven years old at the Restoration, and lived in the reigns of six successive monarchs. Floyer's family were established landowners in Staffordshire and had been prominent in the county for three generations; there were lawyers among its members but none had associations with the profession of medicine. He was the third child of seven in his immediate family, and he decided on a career in medicine.

Floyer followed the standard educational curriculum of his day, beginning with the study of the so-called liberal arts which comprised the *trivium* and *quadrivium* in the Medieval universities of Europe, leading first to the degree of BA and then MA. The medical course at Oxford then required six years residence, attendance at statutory lectures on the writings of Hippocrates and Galen, and the viewing of two or three "anatomies", demonstrations which went on for three days or so, while the dissection of the body of a recently hanged criminal was carried out, if and when available. A striking deficiency in Floyer's education was the absence of clinical teaching involving hospital patients. Thus, in many ways, this system of medical education remained rooted in its Medieval heritage.

However, an intellectual atmosphere and spirit of enquiry in natural philosophy and medicine, much of it emanating from outside the University, pervaded Oxford at the time, and it left a great impact on Floyer. Many of the virtuosi who founded London's Royal Society were in Oxford during the Commonwealth and tended to gather in the warden's lodgings in Wadham College. The Rev. John Wilkins (1614-1672), the warden of Wadham, was tolerant, perceptive and understanding, as well as himself having an interest in experiments. Wilkins invited Robert Boyle

1

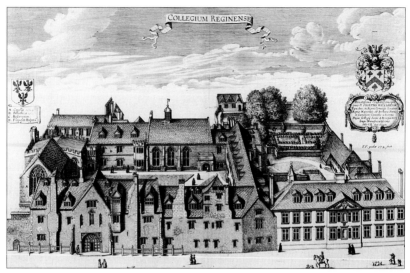

Fig. 2. *The Queen's College, from David Loggan's* Oxonia Illustrata *(1675).*

(1627-1691) to come to Oxford in order to "quicken and direct us in your enquiries".[2] Boyle wrote of the "delight" he found at Oxford in "a knot of such ingenious and free philosophers, who I can assure you do not only admit and entertain real learning, but cherish and improve it".[3]

Boyle lodged for much of the time he was in Oxford, from 1659 to 1688, in a house in the High Street, opposite The Queen's College (Fig. 2) during the time that Floyer was in residence, where Boyle and Robert Hooke (1635-1703) and their collaborators performed the experiments which laid the foundations of respiratory physiology. Thomas Willis (1621-1675), Richard Lower (1631-1691), Christopher Wren (1632-1723), John Locke (1632-1704) and John Mayow (1643-1679) were outstanding members of Boyle's group – a group nicknamed the "Oxonian Sparkles". These individuals led many advances in instrumental technology, notably in devising, constructing and commissioning barometers and thermometers, and in microscopy. Thus, despite what may seem to have been lacking in the official curriculum for medical students, the intellectual ambience in Oxford was exhilarating, exciting, and filled with extracurricular activity.

After spending some twelve years in Oxford preparing to become a physician (he matriculated at The Queen's College when he was 15 in 1664), Floyer practised throughout the rest of his life as physician in

2

Lichfield. He became active in local affairs and was knighted by Charles II in 1684 for civic rather than medical prominence at the time. As well as being a busy physician with an extensive "riding practice", Sir John was an enthusiastic investigator and author who had been strongly influenced during his formative years as a student in the exciting intellectual atmosphere of post-Restoration Oxford. He made several original and important contributions to medicine, several of which were of lasting significance.

Floyer's predecessor as a physician in Lichfield was Anthony Hewett (c.1603-1684), who graduated from Cambridge and Padua, whence he brought back important Renaissance medical books, which Floyer later acquired. Several, notably a book by Santorio Santorio [Sanctorius 1561-1636] of Padua, had a major influence on the direction of Floyer's enquiries, particularly concerning measurement in medicine. (Fig. 3) Though Floyer often did not know how best to apply the data he accumulated and at times was rather overwhelmed with information, in several respects he was a true pioneer. For instance, as well as timing the pulse, he was the first to count respiration rates and to discover an approximate ratio between rates of pulse and respiration; he was also among the first to publish medical data in tabulated form. Citing his own works as "experiments" suggests Floyer's adherence to evidence substantiated by the New Science, i.e., that method of gaining knowledge through an inductive method as proposed in Sir Francis Bacon's *Novum Organon* (1620) and expounded by the work of the Royal Society.

Four works by Floyer are conventionally considered to be historically his most significant. These include:

A Treatise of the Asthma. Divided into Four Parts. In the First is given a History of the Fits and the Symptoms Preceding Them. In the Second, the Cacochymia which Disposes to the Fit, and the Rarefaction of the Spirits which Produces it, are Described. In the Third, the Accidental Causes of the Fit, and the Symptomatic Asthmas are Observed. In the Fourth, the Cure of the Asthma Fit and the Method of Preventing it is Proposed. To which is Annexed a Digression about the Several Species of Acids Distinguish'd by their Tastes. And 'tis Observed how far they were thought Convenient or Injurious in General Practice by the Old Writers, and Most Particularly in Relation to the Cure of Asthma.

(London: R. Wilkin, 1698).

The Ancient ΨΥΧΡΟΛΥΣΙΑ Revived; or, An Essay to Prove Cold Bathing both Safe and Useful. In Four Letters.

Letter I. Concerning the Antiquity of Religious and Medicinal Immersion.

3

Letter II. An Account given of Hippocrates's Opinion, Concerning the Nature of Cold Baths, and their Usefulness.

Letter III. The Ancient Immersion in Baptism is Described, and that it Continued in England, till about the Year 1600 and was also Useful to Cure many Infirmities in Infants, and Prevent Hereditary Diseases, is Clearly Proved.

Letter IV. Describing some Remarkable Cures Done Anciently or Lately by Cold Bathing.

Also a Letter of Dr. Baynard's Containing an Account of Many Eminent Cures done by the Cold Baths in England. Together with a Short Discourse of the Wonderful Virtues of the Bath-Waters on Decayed Stomachs, Drank Hot from the Pump.

(London: S. Smith and B. Walford, 1702)

The Physician's Pulse-Watch; or, An Essay to Explain the Old Art of Feeling the Pulse, and to Improve it by the Help of a Pulse-Watch. In Three Parts.

I. The Old Galenic Art of Feeling the Pulse is Describ'd, and Many of its Errors Corrected: the True Use of the Pulses, and their Causes, Differences and Prognostications by them, are Fully Explain'd, and Directions given for Feeling the Pulse by the Pulse-Watch, or Minute-Glass.

II. A New Mechanical Method is Propos'd for Preserving Health, and Prolonging Life, and for Curing Diseases by the Help of the Pulse-Watch, which Shows the Pulses when they Exceed or are Deficient from the Natural.

III. The Chinese Art of Feeling the Pulse is Describ'd; and the Imitation of their Practice of Physick, which is Grounded on the Observation of the Pulse, is Recommended.

To which is Added, an Extract out of Andrew Cleyer, Concerning the Chinese Art of Feeling the Pulse.

(London: S. Smith and B. Walford, 1707).

The Pulse Watch, Vol II; or, An Essay to Discover the Causes of Diseases and a Rational Method of Curing them by Feeling the Pulse. These Essays are Added as an Appendix:

I. An Essay to Make a New Sphygmologia, by Accommodating the Chinese and the European Observations about the Pulse.

II. An Enquiry into the Nature, Use, Causes and Differences of the Respiratory and the Prognostications which may be Made by them in Diseases.

4

III. A Letter Concerning the Rupture in the Lungs which is the Cause of the Asthma in Mankind, and of the Broken Wind in Horses, and of the Crocke in Hawks, with the Palliative Cure of those Several Diseases and their Symptoms.

(London: J. Nicholson, W. Taylor and H. Clements, 1710).

Medicina Gerocomica; or, The Galenic Art of Preserving Old Men's Healths, Explain'd in Twenty Chapters.

(London, J. Isted, 1724).

He was also the author of several other books that throw light on his interests and enthusiasms. Perhaps inevitably, several subjects he chose for investigation defied accurate analysis, one example of which was his attempts over many years to analyse the therapeutic properties of plants by their tastes and smells.

Links between Lichfield and Oxford in Floyer's Day

Elias Ashmole (1617-1692), a self-made man of prodigious interests, activities and achievements was the son of a saddler in Lichfield. He went to the Grammar school in Lichfield and throughout his life remained intensely loyal to the city of his birth and upbringing. Floyer would have been familiar with Ashmole's prominence in the life of the nation around the time of the Restoration and of his subsequent influence and contributions in Oxford; he respected and admired Ashmole as a famous Royalist son of Lichfield.

Ashmole was also a genealogist, historian, gatherer of folklore, collector and cataloguer of natural and antiquarian "rarities", student of magic, alchemist, astrologer, influential mason, and a founder member of the Royal Society.[4] His crowning achievement was the establishment in Oxford of an institution where the Tradescant family's collections, which he had catalogued, could be preserved and the "knowledge of Nature" could be acquired through the "inspection of particulars".

Though Floyer had been in practice as a physician in Lichfield for several years by the time Ashmole's Museum opened, his contacts with Oxford remained close, particularly with Dr Robert Plot (1640-1696), who was appointed by Ashmole in 1683 to be the first Keeper of the Museum and the first Professor of Chymistry. Plot's pioneering book, *The Natural History of Oxford-shire, being an Essay Toward the Natural History of England,* was published in 1677 and was followed nine years later by *The Natural History of Stafford-shire.* Plot's choice of the county of Staffordshire for such a study was an act of homage to his patron, Ashmole. Over several years while continuing with his commitments in Oxford, Plot gathered data in Staffordshire as opportunity allowed. Plot became well

5

acquainted with John Floyer and other members of the Floyer family in and around Lichfield. The engraved illustration in Plot's book on Staffordshire that portrays a "monstrous birth" (an illustration now recognizable as a teratoma) was dedicated to John Floyer. Such *lusus naturae* or sports of nature, monsters, aberrations and deformities, fascinated virtuosi of the time and led to strange theories and speculations concerning their medical and theological significance.[5]

Floyer shared other interests with Plot. Plot's discussion of the springs and waters of Oxfordshire and Staffordshire in his natural history writing, *De Origine Fontium [Origin of Springs]* (1684), anticipated and perhaps contributed to Floyer's enthusiasm for the subject.[6] In October 1683, Plot revived and reorganised the Oxford Philosophical Society of which Floyer became a member a year later. Although there is no evidence that Floyer attended meetings in Oxford at that stage of his career, membership increased his opportunities for keeping in touch with fellow virtuosi.

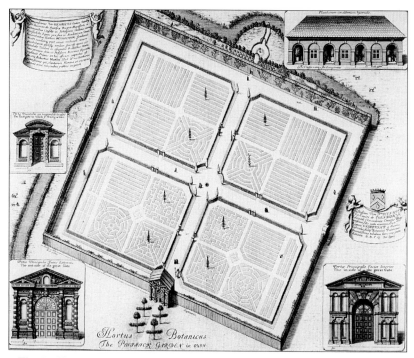

Fig. 3. Hortus Botanicus, *The Physick Garden in Oxford, from David Loggan, Oxonia Illustrata (1675).*

6

Floyer's Oxford experience was also remarkable for indoctrinating him with a life-long passion for botany. The Physic Garden in Oxford (Fig. 3), modelled on similar physic gardens in Padua, Paris and Leiden was the first of its kind in Britain. It was planned and laid out in 1621 on five acres of land, adjoining the river Cherwell opposite Magdalen College. The garden was enclosed by walls, with access through a handsome gateway designed by Inigo Jones (1573-1652) and named after Henry Danvers, Earl of Danby (1573-1644), the chief benefactor of the garden. Planting began in 1642 with the appointment of Jacob Bobart (1621-1680) as its first *Horti Praefectus*. Bobart taught informal classes and led "herborizing" expeditions. By Floyer's time in Oxford as a medical student, the Garden offered considerable opportunities for gaining knowledge and experience in medical botany. As such, it met its original design of supporting the teaching of herbal medicine. In the afternoons, medical students would visit the Garden to taste the plants used in physic and to arrange them according to tastes: mucilaginous, acid, styptic, sweet, oily, bitter, acrid, aromatic, foetid and corrosive. Accordingly, by the prevailing tastes, the plants were reduced into classes appropriate for particular diseases.

Botany was taught to medical students by lectures, by demonstrations and by "simplings" or "herborizings", which were supervised expeditions to study local flora of medical interest.[7] Robert Morison (1620-1683) was appointed Professor of Botany at Oxford in 1669. He lectured in courses that took place twice a year, in May and September. These lectures to considerable audiences were conducted in the middle of the Physic Garden, at a table which was covered with botanical specimens. Each course consisted of three lectures a week for five weeks.[8] An idea of the scope involved in the contemporary botany experience is given in the title page of a small book by William Coles (1626-1662), *The Art of Simpling. An Introduction to the Knowledge and Gathering of Plants, wherein the Definitions, Divisions, Places, Descriptions, Differences, Names, Vertues, Times of Flourishing and Gathering, Uses, Temperatures, Signatures and Appropriations of Plants are Methodically Laid Down* (London: Brook, 1656). The author dedicated the book to "the most exquisite lover of plants, Elias Ashmole, Esq.".

Floyer was educated in Oxford at a time when early forms of the chemical analysis of waters, pioneered particularly by Robert Boyle, were being undertaken. But Floyer was more concerned with water as therapy than in the experimental analysis of water. In his professional career, Floyer agreed with the spa physician, Edward Jorden (1569-1632), who commented on the need for physicians to consider the "many cautions and observations in the bathing, drawn from the particular constitutions of bodies; from the complications of diseases, and from many other

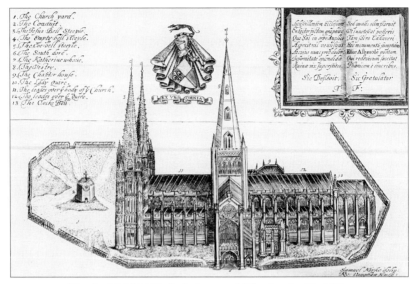

Fig. 4. *Lichfield Cathedral, restored following the Civil War.*

circumstances which cannot be comprehended in general rules, or applied to all bodies alike".[9]

Upon settling in Lichfield, Floyer became more interested in mineral waters and baths, both subjects of topical interest in Post-Restoration England (Fig. 4).[10] At first, he recommended the temperate waters of Buxton, as well as favouring two cold baths in Staffordshire and one in Warwickshire. Later he launched an appeal for the construction of cold baths in Lichfield, for use under his supervision. Between 1697 and 1702, Floyer arranged for the funding and construction of St Chad's Bath at Unite's Well, Abnalls, a mile southwest of Lichfield (Fig. 5). The project was encouraged by the landowner and was subsidized by local gentry. Separate baths for men and women were built. Using a thermometer, Floyer had determined that the spring water at Unite's Well was the coldest in the locality.[11]

Over the course of a career, Floyer became an ardent protagonist of cold bathing and wrote more fully on this subject in a 1702 essay dedicated "to all those worthy and obliging gentlemen, who have contributed towards the erecting [of] the cold bath at Litchfield" (Fig. 6). In this work, he used detailed historical argument to justify cold bathing. He also supported the medical view that many afflictions of the time had resulted from a dietary hot regimen, which had become popular since the

8

Fig. 5. *View towards the City of Lichfield from near Floyer's Cold Bath at Unite's Well, R. Plot,* Natural History of Stafford-shire *(1686).*

Fig. 6. *Floyer's Cold Bath at Abnalls near Lichfield, sketched by Richard Greene, Apothecary, 1770* (Bodleian Library, G.A. Staffs 4°8, opp. p.563).

9

opening up of trade with the Indies, and which was unsuited to English constitutions. He commented that "physicians oft find it a difficult task to conquer the aversions of nice patients, and to persuade them to use those medicines to which they have not been accustomed, until they have convinced them that the medicines are both safe and necessary. I expect to find the same aversion to cold bathing". In justification, he invoked both ancient precedent and recent experience: "none will deny that the method is safe, which has long been tried by the ancient physicians; and, again, lately tried and well experimented by the modern doctors".[12]

Floyer's Books in the Library of The Queen's College, Oxford

In 1724, when he was aged 75, Floyer gave a collection of books and unpublished manuscripts to The Queen's College Oxford, where he had matriculated some sixty years previously (Fig. 7).[13] Among these were a few books he used when he was a student in Oxford, but the great majority he acquired during his long and distinguished career in Lichfield. On blank pages in many of the books and sometimes on printed pages, Floyer wrote comments, notes and prescriptions, as well as adding marginal annotations. Whereas he used some of the books in support of his medical practice, others had been acquired to assist him in his research and writings on medical theory.

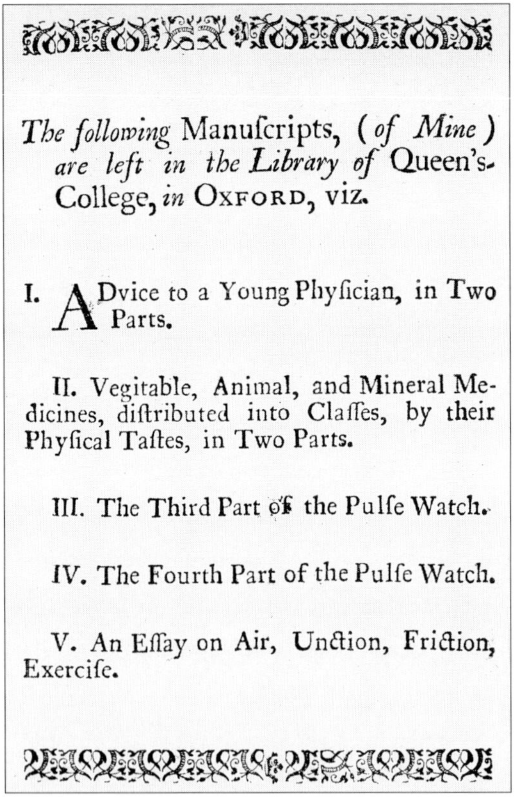

The Floyer collection is similar in some respects to the library of Dr Claver Morris (1659-1726).[14] Ten years younger than Floyer, Morris had also

The following Manuscripts, (*of Mine*) *are left in the Library of* Queen's College, *in* OXFORD, VIZ.

I. A Dvice to a Young Physician, in Two Parts.

II. Vegitable, Animal, and Mineral Medicines, distributed into Classes, by their Physical Tastes, in Two Parts.

III. The Third Part of the Pulse Watch.

IV. The Fourth Part of the Pulse Watch.

V. An Essay on Air, Unction, Friction, Exercise.

Fig. 7. *Notice inserted in* Medicina Gerocomica *(1724) of some manuscripts deposited by Floyer in the Library of The Queen's College, Oxford.*

10

been awarded an MD from Oxford, and he followed a similar career as a provincial physician with a demanding "riding" practice in the cathedral city of Wells; he was also a Tory and a High Churchman with an interest in theological controversy. Unlike Floyer, he kept neat records noting the books he bought and how much he paid for them. He had interests outside his practice, notably in music for relaxation, and also, as an offshoot of his medical interests, he enjoyed carrying out experiments in chemistry in his own laboratory. Again, in marked contrast to Floyer, Morris did not aspire to be an author of medical or theological works, so that he did not obtain his books for that purpose.

A special feature of the Floyer collection is that it not only reflects the working library of a busy provincial physician of the period, but it also contains much of the source material upon which Floyer relied when writing his important medical works. In this respect, the collection provides a unique resource for the interpretation and understanding of Floyer's contributions, offering continuing opportunities for the further assessment of his place in the history of medicine, as well as for more general studies on the nature of the practice of an important provincial physician of the time.

There are many ways in which the close links and associations of the collection with Floyer are evident. For instance, he included nearly all the books he had written and that had been published by then, several of which contain additional notes written in his hand. Representative of the books he used when he was a medical student, are two small vellum-covered volumes (1669 and 1672) by Paul Barbette (c. 1623-1666), with interleaved blank pages on which Floyer has written many notes in Latin, mainly on the subject of pharmaceutical ingredients and prescriptions; on a front page of one of the volumes, he later wrote "these collected in my younger days". Probably the most personal of all the holdings is the manuscript which Floyer wrote on *Directions for the Education of My Grandchild John Floyer in the Study of Physic*; sadly, his infant grandson died at the age of four.

As previously mentioned, Floyer was preceded in Lichfield by the physician Anthony Hewett who had for many years been the only university-trained physician practising in that region. Throughout his Continental travels, Hewett acquired a number of important Renaissance medical books which, together with those he subsequently bought in England, Floyer later acquired. Perhaps Hewett had no further use for his books by then, or possibly Floyer bought them from Hewett's estate, after his death in 1684. Floyer noted the authors and prices that he paid for books on the endpapers of one of Hewett's books. Fortunately it is possible to identify these books which came from Hewett into Floyer's possession and which were in due course included in his gift to The

Queen's College, by the small monogram which Hewett neatly inscribed on the title pages of his books. Only recently, as a result of the identification of Hewett's books as an important part of the Floyer collection, has Hewett himself been rescued from obscurity and is now belatedly recognised as a physician of some consequence who practised in Lichfield in the middle years of the 17th century.[15]

Floyer was fortunate to acquire these books at a time when he had entered a remarkably productive and formative period of his life. Several of these books greatly influenced Floyer and shaped the direction of his endeavours. For instance, *De Medicatis Aquis* (1564), by Gabriele Falloppio [Fallopius] (1523-1562), promoted the revival of medical interest in waters and bathing, about which Floyer became enthusiastic, writing extensively on the subject.[16]

The provenances of several other books in the Floyer collection are of interest. A late printed copy of *Rosa Anglica* (1595) belonged to William, 5th Baron Digby of Coleshill, who was a friend and patient of Floyer; it seems likely that he gave the book to Floyer as a present. A more important book for Floyer was *Specimen Medicinae Sinicae* (1682) by Andreas Cleyer (1634-1697/98); it was at first lent and then given to him in 1706, by the Honourable Charles Hatton (1635-*c*.1708).[17] Floyer was intrigued by the descriptions given in this book about Chinese pulse-lore and acupuncture, which he proceeded to translate from Latin and which formed the basis for the first significant publication in English on these subjects.[18] Floyer probably acquired most of his books by purchase rather than as gifts. Two can be identified as coming from Michael Johnson's bookshop in Lichfield, where he probably placed orders for other books. Michael Johnson, the father of Samuel Johnson, and Floyer were friends and fellow churchwardens of neighbouring parish churches in Lichfield.

The range of subjects and authors represented in the collection reflects Floyer's wide interests in both the practical and theoretical aspects of the medicine of his time, including areas of alchemy and Paracelsian medicine. The perennial need to prescribe and to advise on appropriate treatments for patients has been an important concern of physicians in all periods of history. Throughout his years of practice, Floyer made sure that he had suitable books to assist him, for example *The Compleat Chymical Dispensatory* (1669) by Johann Schröder, Pharmacopoeias compiled by Bate (1688) and Fuller (1701), and the Pharmacopoeia of the Royal College of Physicians (4th edition, 1721), in which he made many notes. One of the last books Floyer bought, less than a year before he gave his collection to the College, was a book of lectures on therapeutics, *Praelectiones Pharmaceuticae; or, A Course of Lectures in Pharmacy, Chymical and Galenical; Explaining the Whole Doctrine of the Art, by the late learned Dr. John Quincy, published from his Original Manuscript, with a Preface, by P. Shaw, M.D.* (1723).

Floyer's Manuscripts in The Library of The Queen's College, Oxford

As part of the Wellcome Trust Project on Research Sources in Medical History in 2003, a *Catalogue of the Manuscripts of Sir John Floyer, The Queen's College, University of Oxford* has recently been compiled by Mary Clapinson (2004, Fig. 8).[19] For purposes of classification, the Floyer MSS. have been categorised as medical (The Queen's College MSS. 558-569) or theological (MSS. 570-581), although there is considerable overlap of subject matter in some of the manuscripts.[20]

MS. 558 is a treatise by Floyer in paper wrappers,

Fig. 8. *The Library, The Queen's College, Oxford.*

entitled *Advise to a Young Student in Physicke* (Fig. 9), which is made up of the following folios: (fols. 2-10) Evidence Provided by the Mechanisms of the Human Body for the Existence of God the Creator; (fols. 11-14) God as "The Author of the Art of Physicke" and Characteristics of a Good Physician; (fols. 15-21) The Academic and Practical Education of a Physician, including (fol.21) A Scheme for the Establishment of a Medical College at Oxford University and the Foundation of a Hospital there for the Care of the Poor and the Instruction of Students; (fol. 22) The Charity and Compassion of a

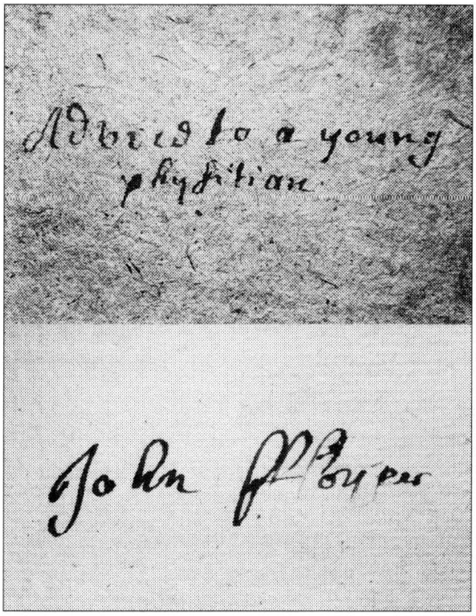

Fig. 9. *Floyer's handwritten title of* Advice to a Young Physician.

13

Good Physician, who should Attend the Poor Free of Charge; (fols. 23-26) The Ethics of Medical Practice; (fols.27-30) The Characteristics of a Poor Physician; and (fol. 28) The Causes of "Disgrace in Physicke in this Age". These sections have been included in the present publication and the chapter headings used by Floyer have been retained. The subsequent folios in MS. 558 on the following subjects which were somewhat removed from the theme of medical education have been omitted: The Improvement of Clinical Practice by the Study and Application of Medicines According to their Tastes (fols. 31-45); An Account of Ancient Practice in the Prescription of "Hot" Medicines for "Cold Diseases" and of "Cold Specifics for Hott Diseases" (fol. 46); and Observations on the Effects of Cold and Hot Baths (fols. 47-48).

Floyer gave the title *Physicall Essayes; or, The First Part of a Dispensatory for the Countrey Physician* to a manuscript now catalogued as MS. 559, on page one of which he wrote a list of six subjects he presented as essays, as follows: 1. Instruction for the Young Student in the Art of Physicke; 2. The Forms of Medicines Distinguished by their General Tastes and the Best Forms Collected from Bate and Fuller and Quincy; 3. Tables of Vegitables Digested by their Physical Tastes and the Animal and Mineral Medicines According to their Tastes; 4. An Essay on the Quantity of Alteratives; 5. A Specimen of a Collection of our Countrey Receipts under their General Tastes; 6. A Scheme of the Variety of Pulses in Most Diseases. It is thus apparent that most of MS. 559 is devoted to subjects which reflected Floyer's interest in medicines, recipes and receipts, and the fascination he had during most of his adult life for the exploration of tastes, with the hope of making useful taxonomic and therapeutic discoveries. Only MS.559 fol.2, which is referred to in Floyer's list as *Instruction for the Young Student in the Art of Physic* and was headed by him *Directions for the Education of my Grandchild John Floyer in the Study of Physick*, has been included in this publication.

Floyer added a note he wrote in different ink, "writt before his death", to his heading for this essay. Sir John Floyer's only grandson, like his father and grandfather before him, was also named John Floyer. John Floyer (III) was born in September 1716 and died three months after his fourth birthday in December 1720. Sir John's dedication leaves little doubt that he wrote at least this section of MS. 559 during the lifetime of young John Floyer III, between 1716 and 1720. Floyer also wrote a note at the end of the list of contents (MS.559 fol.1), recommending that "the title of all these essays may be the second part of the advice to a young physician".

One further short extract from the corpus of Floyer MSS. is included in this book. It is taken from MS. 566 *An Essay to Improve the Animall Spirits . . . .* , comprising 77 numbered pages and two final pages which

14

are unnumbered. Floyer has headed the last of these two unnumbered pages *Devotions made out of Epictetus's Moralls and Simplicius's Comment.* Though not intended by Floyer to be part of *The Advice to a Young Physician,* it offers a brief insight into certain aspects of Floyer's personal beliefs and philosophy in his later life, at the time he was writing the various papers which have been collected here to form his *Advice.*

Analysis of Floyer's *Advice to a Young Physician*

In order to place medical education of the period into context, concerning both its underlying philosophy and practice, it may be helpful to summarize some particulars. It is our intention to give readers a glimpse of several of the key topics that Floyer introduced in his *Advice,* further illuminating their meaning with select comments from Floyer when possible, and directing them to further historical consideration of these topics. A glossary to aid in the historical understanding of key medical terms is provided following the *Advice.*

"Advice" for University and Medical Education in Floyer's Time

A number of "Advice" manuals concerning education were written during Floyer's lifetime, though not always published at the time. For example, John Evelyn (1620-1706) began writing *Memories for My Grandson* in 1704, filling it with wisdom for approaching character development and education. Regarding education, he claimed that the study of natural philosophy and mathematics "are greatly to be cherish'd & cultivated" and that his grandson should not be "Ignorant of Anatomy, as it concerns your owne Body & its wonderfull structure" which is "a Microcosme" to be appreciated.[21] William Cecil, Lord Burleigh (1520-1598), Sir Walter Raleigh (1552-1618), and Francis Osborne (1593-1659) each prepared personal educational manuals that appeared under the title, *Advice to His Son.*[22] Some schoolmasters and university dons prepared works for their own pupils as well.[23] Daniel Waterland (1683-1740), Dean and then Master of Magdalene College, Cambridge, drew up a "perpetual Guide and Monitor" for the undergraduates of his college in about 1706, which was published in 1730. Acknowledging that although a Tutor may be "ever so diligent", having a "considerable Number of Pupils", he "cannot be so particular and frequent in his Instructions and Advice to each of them as he wished, or may be necessary for their well-doing".[24]

Fewer such manuals appeared regarding "Advice" for medical education and the character development of physicians. Among the known works are John Locke's *De Arte Medica* (1669), Théophile Bonet's *A Guide to the Practical Physician* (1684), Samuel Parker's *Essay upon the Duty of Physicians and Patients* (1715) and somewhat later, Joannes Groenevelt's *The Rudiments of Physick* (1753) and John Gregory's *Lectures on the Duties* and *Qualifications of a Physician* (1772).[25] Groenevelt (ca. 1647-1710) expressed concern that no "proper Regard" had been offered to "the Improvement of the Young Pupil". Rather, most medical authors "write for such as are thoroughly grounded in the Rudiments or Principles of the Art, whereby the Tyro is left greatly at a Loss, and very often never gains a thorough Knowledge of its Principles".[26]

Floyer held strong views concerning the advantages to the medical student of gaining clinical knowledge and experience under the supervision of clinicians and teachers who treated patients in hospital. But such hospital education was not then available in England. "'Tis certainly a great defect in the education of physicians in the universities" of England, Floyer argues, "that none of their professors teach the practical part but only treat their auditors with notions about which all disputes are unnecessary". (34-5)[27] Therefore, he suggests in his *Advice* that "at nineteen let him go into Holland and there see the practice of physic and surgery for two or three years in their hospitals". In the same chapter he gave his opinion more forcefully: "beyond seas the practice of physic will be shown by the professors there; but all time spent by a physician in our universities is misspent, there being no college for physicians nor hospitals for practice". (38) Christopher Wordsworth echoes this sentiment, claiming that though students "might receive the grounds of a valuable education, and some theoretical instruction" in England, they were "obliged to look elsewhere for practical knowledge to qualify them for their profession".[28]

Floyer was insistent that Oxford could improve its own medical educational provisions. Indeed, he wrote *Advice* at a time when the need for some hospital provisions was being more widely recognized and discussed. "If it were possible to erect a hospital in Oxford for the care of the poor, there all the young students would see the practice of physic. And I would advise them to observe first the effects of all the dispensatory medicines and then those of the hospital medicines already published and . . . to observe all the curious chirurgical operations and those in midwifery. The want of such experiments is the occasion of a young physician's want of employment for some years, because in the university he can learn little of the practical part. If the several colleges and the town would join their purses, they might soon erect a hospital for the cure of the poor and the instruction of young students".

Moreover, Floyer envisaged the founding of a College of Physicians in Oxford, to advance teaching and research. "It would not be difficult to institute a college of physicians in Oxford by appointing one of the halls by an Act of Parliament for that profession only. And, by the consent of the several colleges, the physicians who are on their foundations may be transferred and the salary of their fellowships ingrafted in the new physicians' college and there constitute the fellows of that society. And that none should be transferred till they have been two years standing in their original college, nor continue longer in the physicians' college than three years after their doctor's degree. But, when they leave it, they may be obliged to communicate all the rare cases in practice or experiments of our own country medicines to the college. It would be necessary that some eminent apothecary and chirurgeon be admitted into the same college to teach the young students those practical arts first".

"Afterwards let the young student go through a course of anatomy, botany and chymistry and, at last, attend the professors to direct his study and to see their practice upon the poorer sort. The professors of physic, anatomy, chymistry and botany ought to be members of the same foundation and may be chose once in three years by the fellows". This scheme, he concludes, "would improve the faculty by the joint endeavours of many ingenious men and, from this college, expert physicians would be sent into all parts of this kingdom". (34-35)

Evolution and Competition of Medical Theories

Floyer flourished at a time when advocates of the new Baconian Science were questioning and overtaking traditional, ancient models of thinking about the natural world and human bodies. Of importance to physicians, this era challenged the longstanding foundation of Galenic medicine; in particular, the concept of humoural pathology that explained disease in terms of an imbalance of the four humours (i.e., yellow bile, phlegm, blood, and black bile). Healthiness was also thought to be impeded by the non-naturals. Physicians since the time of Galen viewed six "non-natural" causes (namely air, meat and drink, sleep and watching, motion and rest, retention and excretion, and the passions of the mind) as potential causes of disease that were distinct from the natural (innate) causes as well as contra-natural (pathological) causes.[29] In many areas, Floyer remained supportive of Galenic concepts as the basis of his medical thinking. Towards the end of his career, he reaffirmed his conviction that "there is no true method of prolonging our lives, but by the right use of the six non-naturals, by which we may repair our decaying spirits, renew the nutritious humours, and soften and relax the dry and obstructed solids".[30]

One of the rival medical theories of Floyer's era was medicine based predominantly upon historical chemistry: the theory of iatrochemistry. Iatrochemical physicians typically harked back to some aspects of alchemical traditions, viewing human physiology and disease in terms of chemical balances of fluids within the body. Adherents of this school of thought included Jan Baptiste van Helmont (1579-1644), Franciscus Sylvius [François de le Boë] (1614-1672), and Thomas Willis.[31] Distinct from

Galenic doctrine, iatrochemists attempted to restore health through chemically prepared drugs.

Iatrochemical influences were dominant in Oxford during the time of Thomas Willis, Robert Boyle and Robert Plot. Plot, whose *Natural History of Oxford-shire* had prompted Ashmole to seek out Oxford to house his collection of antiquities, was, at the time, also Professor of Chymistry. In the latter capacity, he read "three times a week . . . during the time of the chymical course, which continues an entire month, concerning all natural bodies relating to and made use of in chymical preparations, particularly as to the countries and places where they are produced, and found, their natures, their qualities and virtues, their effects, by what marks and characteristicks they are distinguished one from another, natural from artificial, true from sophisticated, with their several mixtures and preparations in trials and experiments".[32] These efforts, true to Bacon's New Science, attempted to establish a new chemical tradition founded on authentic experimentation rather than exclusively upon alchemical heritage.

During the last third of his life, Floyer was greatly influenced by concepts promoted especially by Giorgio Baglivi (1668-1707) and Herman Boerhaave (1668-1738). Baglivi, as well as carrying out early studies by microscopy on tissue fibres, was also a theorist. Boerhaave extended notions of "fibre pathology" and was authoritative in disseminating the concept that the fibre was "the ultimate locus of disease as well as the ultimate structural unit".[33] Writing in his *Advice*, Floyer recognized the limitations of knowledge at the time concerning both fibres and fluids in the body, when he wrote: "we are not yet fully informed of the nice composition of one fibre and the causes of its motion; nor do we know the composition of one globule in the fluids and how the water, slimy fibres, the oily and the salt are mixed in it; nor where they are separated from each globule by the secretions". Whatever the deficiencies of understanding, simple hypotheses based on changes in fibres, provided a basis for interpreting many medical phenomena and a rationale for some treatments. As an example, Floyer wrote that fibres in children are "lax, soft and flexible, but they grow hard and drier in men, and in the old age, most hard, dry or callous, or wrinkled and varicose by wine, cares and hard labour. We make the solids lax and flexible by baths, hot lotions, fomentations and unctions which have been of late too much disused. We make the fibres more tense by friction, exercise, ustion and cold baths". (41)

Another branch of physicians, later referred to as iatromechanists, viewed the human body in terms of mechanics or machinery. As evident in Floyer's writings, he was greatly influenced by the writings of Sanctorius, Professor of Medicine in Padua and close friend of Galileo. Sanctorius was among the first physicians fully to appreciate how much could be gained from the use of measurement in medicine. But, the measuring devices he used or suggested were, in general, too rudimentary or unwieldy to be as useful as he desired. Nevertheless, his invention of the weighing chair (Fig. 10) for metabolic and balance studies was a triumph, making it possible for him to note and to quantify insensible perspiration. Some 80 years later, Floyer too installed a weighing chair, which he used "after the manner of Sanctorius", on a patient with asthma (himself), before and after attacks.[34]

Fig. 10. *Weighing Chair of Sanctorius, John Quincy,* Medicina Statica: Being the Aphorisms of Sanctorius *(1712).*

Pulse and Circulation

During this time, Floyer's interest in applying measurement to medicine became something of a preoccupation. In many ways, Floyer was an iatromechanist in his thinking. Such thinking is evident in his devotion to pulse-timing, a method for which he is remembered as a pioneer.[35] He was the first person to make numerous observations on pulse rates by means of a specially constructed watch with a second hand. Though Floyer used his pulse watch within a framework of Galenic beliefs, the watch was perhaps the first reasonably efficient clinical instrument to merit application in practice.

Floyer's extensive published writings on pulse timing with the many tables of data he compiled early in the 18th century, are well known. He began by making simple observations with his pulse watch and soon extended these to explore possible relationships between pulse rates and other measurements, such as barometric pressure and ambient temperature, not to mention phases of the moon. Though he was sometimes over ambitious and naïve, particularly when he extrapolated fancifully from the data he collected, he made important and original discoveries, such as observing for the first time an approximate ratio between pulse and respiration rates.

At a time when Floyer was starting his medical practice in 1675, there was a crucial development in horological technology. The introduction of a spring balance was conceived by Robert Hooke, who performed experimental work on the subject as early as 1658. But, it took another 17 years before Thomas Tompion (1639-1713), at Hooke's behest, made a watch for Charles II in 1675, which operated under the control of a spring balance. Though the watch was neither very accurate nor reliable, for the first time in England, the construction of timepieces that showed the passing of seconds as well as of hours and of minutes had become technically feasible.[36]

Floyer's fascination with timing the pulse was also inspired by Sanctorius, particularly from reading the relevant parts of his *Commentary on Avicenna* (1625), a book he acquired from Hewett.[37] Here the many different instruments and apparatus devised by Sanctorius, including several examples of pulsilogiums, were illustrated and discussed. Floyer may well have been as baffled as some readers of the present day in trying to understand precisely how several of Sanctorius's instruments worked; some were probably prototypes rather than of proven value, and most were probably designed with research rather than clinical practice in mind. Floyer took an important initiative by requesting Samuel Watson (*c.* 1635-1710) to construct a pulse-watch with a seconds hand (Fig. 11), soon after the requisite technological advance had been achieved.

In his preface to the first volume of *The Physician's Pulse-Watch*, published in 1707, Floyer referred to the instruments he had used for timing the pulse. "I have for many years tried pulses by the minute in common watches, and pendulum clocks, when I was among my patients; after some time I met with the common sea-minute glass, which I used for my cold bathing, and by that I made most of my experiments; but because this was not portable, I caused a pulse-watch to be made . . .".

Range of Medical Practices in Floyer's Day

Floyer would have been very familiar with the broad range of practitioners existing in his day. Domestic medical manuals were widely available to give helpful hints as to the prevention and treatment of common illnesses.[38] Many physicians, however, viewed such works as opening up the treatment of diseases to a realm of "pretenders" of medicine, or quacks. Others deemed it as quackery when an individual applied a single, universal remedy for the treatment of all diseases. "All pretenders

Fig. 11. *The Physician's Pulse-Watch, commissioned by Floyer and constructed by Samuel Watson.*

to universal medicines", Floyer argued, "meet in time with ill success; their medicines are found to be cheats and disused". (34)

The word 'physic' is derived from the Greek ρλυςις, meaning nature; physic was one of the branches of the study of nature or natural philosophy. University trained physicians, usually qualified with a doctorate of medicine, practised the healing art of physic. According to the medical historian Harold Cook, physicians "had to study natural philosophy because the purposes of physic were to preserve health and prolong life; healing the sick was an important part, but only one of the many parts, of physic. The physician had to be able to offer advice to the healthy as well as to the sick about how to live according to nature, for being in harmony with nature would result in the preservation of health as well as the prolongation of life. Only by studying the principles of natural philosophy rooted in ancient literature and elaborated in contemporary Latinate education could the physician understand how nature worked well enough to carry out his tasks".[39]

Attesting to Floyer's reliance upon Hippocrates, we find his incorporation of Hippocratic aphorisms throughout the *Advice*. For example, "Whosoever considers the art necessary for the study of a physician and that he must consider a long experience in that art to acquire any judgement in it, will admire the industry of such a person". Furthermore, he specifies that Hippocrates provided the "examples we ought to imitate". (28)[40] Indeed, it has been common throughout Western history for physicians to refer back to Hippocrates as their true mentor of medical practice.

Another way in which Floyer exemplified Hippocratic practice is evident from his emphasis on the use of senses in his practice of medicine.[41] "God has given us our senses whereby, with the help of experiments, we can discern the virtues of all our medicines. By their tastes and smells we know their qualities: hot medicines which accelerate our circulations, and all the cold tastes which stop the vehemency of it and the secretions. And, by our senses, we can discern the natural and the preternatural state of humours, which are the antecedent causes of our diseases". (6)

One sense, in particular, was of elevated importance for Floyer: the sense of taste. Nehemiah Grew (1641-1712), born in Mancetter, between Lichfield and Coventry, had initiated new interest in plant physiology in England with his influential *The Anatomy of Plants*, published in 1682.[42] This work expanded the understanding of the function of "plant tissue", particularly by extending knowledge by means of the newly available microscopy. It also attracted the interest of physicians who, like Floyer, wished to further their understanding of the properties and actions of plants when concocted into medicines. Grew discussed the therapeutic properties of plants in relation to their tastes, an interest that we see Floyer also developed. Indeed, it formed the subject of Floyer's first book, *The Touch-stone of Medicines* (1687).

Floyer believed that the virtues of medicines are best discovered by their tastes and by frequent experiments made of them on our bodies. In his *Touch-stone of Medicines*, Floyer discusses how this interest was developed with tasting the Jesuits' Bark (*Cortex peruvianus*) while in Oxford, the effects of which gave him the "first occasion of inquiring into the tastes of the barks of trees in our country" such that he "might find which were like it" and from there he "proceeded to inquire into the tastes of herbs". After Floyer started in practice in Lichfield, he visited John Watts (fl. 1670-1690), who had recently been appointed Gardner at the newly-established Physic Garden of the Society of Apothecaries in Chelsea. Floyer claimed that Watts' taste and smell of plants "did very much agree with mine", such that he "readily acknowledge[d] my right classing of many plants".[43] In Lichfield, Floyer enlisted the assistance of many friends, colleagues, and patients. He did not have absolute trust in his own taste "in the description of our country herbs", and "he therefore consulted the tastes of all sorts of persons, and for that I am oblig'd to divers divines, apothecaries, chyrurgeons, gentlewomen and young persons, who have been patients; whose judgement as Galen says is uncorrupt and unprejudiced".

It is by testing the taste and smell of a medicine, Floyer claimed, that "the true physician knoweth its virtues, the manner of its preparation, the suitableness of it to the humour to be connected, and to the constitution of the patients, all of which the quack is ignorant".[44]

Turning to Floyer's *Advice*, we find that "God has endowed our medicines with various tastes and smells and, by them, we know their virtues and cure diseases by contrary tastes; and this is a full proof that He is the author of physic. By our tastes and smells we discover the virtues of diet and medicines and then, by our reason and experience, we are taught to use contrary tastes to the diseased quality of our humour which produce any diseased action". (5) Elsewhere he argued, "Chymistry only separates the principles but cannot discover the qualities produced by their mixture. We never can discover the texture, figure or proportion of the particles of our medicines; the sensible quality is all we know and all that is necessary. The fire destroys all mucilages and the chymist medicines want that taste. We cure diseases by contrary tastes: the watery, acid, styptic and mucilagenous tastes correct the bitter, salt and acrid humours, by cooling and diluting them; and the acrid, bitter, salt [and] sweet correct mucilagenous humours by fermenting, inciding and attenuating of them". (57)

Contained in the dedication Floyer wrote for volume one of his first book, *The Touch-stone of Medicines* (1687), is a statement of the purpose of his studies on tastes and smells. "The design of this essay is to vindicate the art of curing diseases from the common scandal of being conjectural, by describing the tastes and odours of medicines and also the animal humours for, by these, medicines were first discovered and the humours of the body examined; and from the observation of the agreement and contraries betwixt the taste of the humours in the body and the medicine, it was easy for physicians to infer that, by a medicine of the same taste, the humours of the body are preserved and, by contrary taste in the medicine, they are altered and corrected." In his preface addressed to the reader of the same book, Floyer explained in more detail his hopes and what he anticipated would be the rewards to be expected from analysis by means of the senses of taste and smell. For Floyer it proved to be a lifelong endeavour. "I hope I shall make it manifest in the ensuing discourse, that there is no virtue yet known in plants but what depends on the taste and smell, and may be known by them. This was certainly the foundation on which the old physicians raised the art of physic, but they were strangely led from it by Aristotle's philosophy, which taught them to express the virtues of medicines by hot, cold, moist and dry (and by occult qualities), to which they attributed all effects, neglecting the information of their senses. But we now have more advantages than (in) the former ages. By chymistry we distinguish the principles which produce each taste; and the learned Mr Boyle hath given us a clear and satisfactory account of qualities. The famous Malpighius [sic] and ingenious Dr Grew have discovered the several vessels of plants and the last has given us his curious reflections upon tastes".[45]

The Religion of a Physician

Throughout the *Advice*, there are frequent reminders of Floyer's recognition of a divine plan and purpose, and of his consciousness of the divine origin and endowment of life. The laws of nature that were being discovered during Floyer's day were considered, by many, to have been laid down by God at the time of the Creation. Such truths were part of a revealed religion that was underlying much of his Oxford experience and, like illustrious contemporaries such as John Ray (1627-1705) and Isaac Newton (1642-1727), Floyer believed that the world had been created less than six thousand years ago.[46]

The developing iatromechanistic explanation for many physical processes was adduced to support arguments in favour of natural religion. Boyle wrote extensively concerning discoveries in natural philosophy which strengthened his Christian beliefs. Ray, for example, stated this position with the well-chosen title of his popular book, *The Wisdom of God Manifested in the Works of Creation* (1691).[47] During Floyer's lifetime, the role of reason was magnified and that of revelation reduced. The scriptures were intensively scrutinized, miracles challenged, and prophesies reassessed. The balance shifted from what God had revealed to what man had discovered. In England the challenge to the Christian faith was met with vigour and determination. Floyer adhered to the old tenets and made his own attempts to integrate the new thoughts and discoveries of the age into traditional belief and into the teaching of the Church. He took it for granted that the young physician to whom he addressed his *Advice* would be interested in such matters and would understand their relevance to his education, outlook, and practice.

The theological discussions in *Advice* may sometimes present difficulties to present-day readers, particularly those who are relatively unversed, for example, in concepts of the soul, the status of angels, and the finer details expounded in the book of Revelations. Floyer became particularly obscure in some of his later published work on prophecies and chronology but, as usual, in his interests and writings, he was reflecting particular enthusiasms of the time. It should be remembered here that Isaac Newton in his later life, devoted the majority of his time to exploring prophecies and establishing Biblical chronology.[48]

Influenced by Boyle, Ray and many others at the time with similar beliefs, Floyer in his *Advice* viewed the study of physic, that is of nature, as a way of understanding more of God's wisdom and plan. "You will have sufficient evidence from the fabric of the body and circulation and the secretions of humours that there is a God that made it; and believe that he appointed you to the art of preserving that curious machine and to cure its defects. And that he has obliged you to be industrious, compassionate, charitable, humble, prudent in words and easy in conversation and, above all, to depend on the Creator of human bodies for your success in preserving its life and operation for the term he has appointed you to it".

"My last observation shall be that God usually determines, by some second causes, every man to some particular employment or profession. He requires some public service of every person, as soon as he attains to a mature age: that he either employ his body or mind to serve some end of providence. And, if we do some useful service to the public or our neighbour, we thereby serve God and shall receive a reward in this life or the next for employing our talent well". (34-35)

Chapter 1

Directions for the Education of my Grandchild John Floyer in the Study of Physic (Fig. 12)

LET HIM CONTINUE at school till he can translate any Latin author into English and from the English into proper Latin; and collect French grammar to teach him to speak it commonly. And let him have so much Greek as to construe his Greek testament perfectly. The making of themes

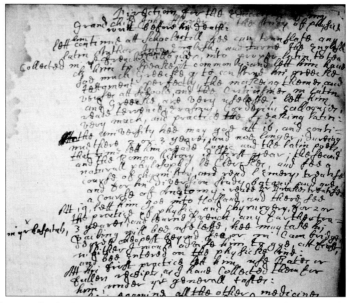

Fig. 12. *Beginning of Floyer's "Directions for the Education of My Grandchild in the Study of Physic" in his* Advice *manuscript, the Library, The Queen's College, Oxford.*

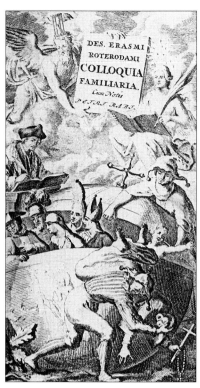

Fig. 13. *Desiderius Erasmus,* Colloquia Familiaria *(1693).*

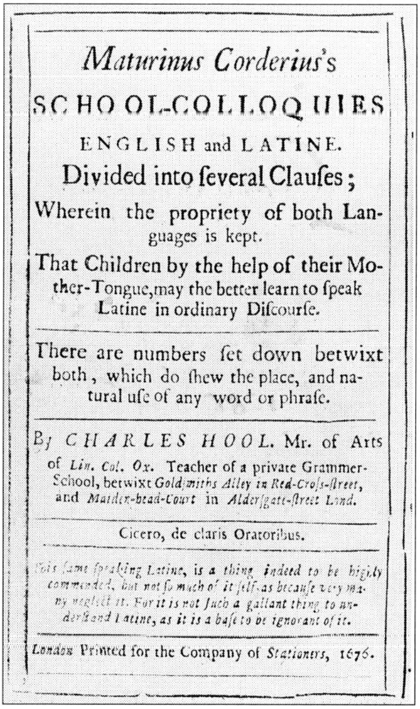

Maturinus Corderius's

SCHOOL-COLLOQUIES

ENGLISH and LATINE.

Divided into ſeveral Clauſes;

Wherein the propriety of both Languages is kept.

That Children by the help of their Mother-Tongue, may the better learn to ſpeak Latine in ordinary Diſcourſe.

There are numbers ſet down betwixt both, which do ſhew the place, and natural uſe of any word or phraſe.

By *CHARLES HOOL*. Mr. of Arts of *Lin. Col. Ox.* Teacher of a private Grammer-School, betwixt *Goldſmiths Alley in Red-Croſs-ſtreet*, and *Maiden-head-Court* in *Alderſgate-ſtreet Lond.*

Cicero, de claris Oratoribus.

This ſame ſpeaking Latine, is a thing indeed to be highly commended, but not ſo much of it ſelf as becauſe very many neglect it. For it is not ſuch a gallant thing to underſtand Latine, as it is a baſe to be ignorant of it.

London Printed for the Company of *Stationers*, 1676.

Fig. 14. *Maturinus Corderius,* School Colloquies *(1676).*

and verses at school, and the criticisms in Latin and Greek are very useless. Let him read Terence[49] and the *Colloquies* of Erasmus (Fig. 13)[50] and Corderius (Fig. 14),[51] very much, and practise the speaking Latin. To the university he may go at sixteen and continue there two or three years and no longer. During that time let him read logic and the Latin poets and Roman history at first year; the second natural philosophy (Le Clerc),[52] and see a course of chymistry and read Lemery's[53] treatise; and, for his diversion, study botany and get a course of anatomy (read Dr Drake's treatise) (Fig. 15).[54]

At nineteen let him go into Holland and there see the practice of physic and chirurgery for two or three years in their hospitals,[55] and learn French; any further travelling will be useless. He may take his degree cheapest beyond sea or in Cambridge, whither I would advise him to go first and be entered on the physic line.

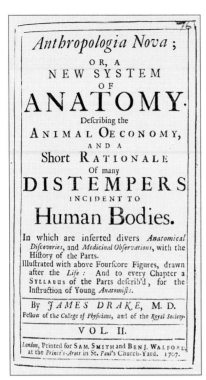
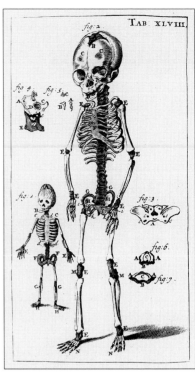

Fig. 15. *James Drake,* Anthropologia Nova: or, A New System of
Anatomy *(1707).*

At his first practice let him use Bate's[56] or Fuller's (Fig. 16)[57] receipts
under their several tastes. Let him examine all the other medicines by their
tastes and smells, and reduce them into their classes; for, if you know of
the taste, that will discover its dose, quantity and the cause of the disease
which it can cure, and in what constitutions it is proper.

Let him discover the pulses in every disease (and) the alteration of
them and how to direct his practice by them (Fig. 17). I have given a short
scheme of diseases and their pulses and, when he reads physic I have left
a book of pulses for him and a second and third part of *The Pulse-watch*
to direct him. *The Preternatural State of Animal Humours* will show the
general cacochymias or qualities in my book of them.[58] Then read the
diseases from the motion of the humours and those from viscidity of the
blood and then (those) from the great quantity and evacuations and, at
last, those diseases from the oppression of the circulatory organs or their
irritation.

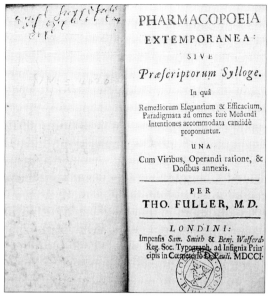

Fig. 16. *Floyer's copy of Thomas Fuller,* Pharmacopoeia Extemporanea *(1701),*
the Library, The Queen's College, Oxford.

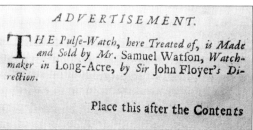

Fig. 17. *Advertisement in Floyer's* Physician's Pulse-Watch *(1707).*

29

He may compare Riverius's[59] and Ettmüller's (Fig. 18)[60] practice at the same time, reading in the same diseases; and Dr Willis.[61] Read those authors who treat on any single disease they know of: vide my *Treatise of the Asthma,*[62] Morton *De Febribus,*[63] Lower *De Corde*[64] or Strother *Criticon Febrium.*[65] Sylvius,[66] Willis, Sydenham,[67] Galen and Hippocrates[68] may be read upon long practice. Forestus's *Practice*[69] is very useful; and Sennertus (Fig.19).[70]

I have made a small collection of simple medicines which will be useful to the poor and left a larger collection transcribed and more expertly digested under their specific tastes. These may be useful in country practice, but the extemporaneous forms are first to be used by young practicers in towns to oblige the apothecary and to promote business.

If he ever undertakes country practice he cannot soon get into much business unless he practise chirurgery as well as physic and have knowledge in midwifery.[71] These may be learnt in hospitals beyond sea.

It will be of great advantage to visit chalybeate springs, Bath and the cold baths, and observe the practice and success there (Fig. 20).[72]

Beyond seas the practice of physic will be shown by the professors there. But all the time spent by a physician in our universities after two or three years is misspent, there being no college for physicians nor hospitals for practice. A nice[73] enquiry into anatomy, chymistry, mathematics and botany will misspend our time and is useless to a practiser in physic.

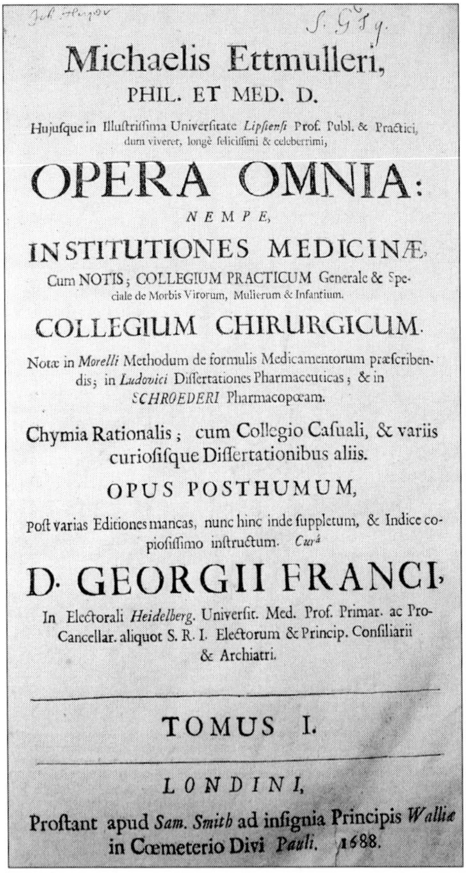

Michaelis Ettmulleri,
PHIL. ET MED. D.
Hujuſque in Illuſtriſſima Univerſitate *Lipſienſi* Prof. Publ. & Practici, dum viveret, longè feliciſſimi & celeberrimi,

OPERA OMNIA:
NEMPE,
INSTITUTIONES MEDICINÆ,
Cum NOTIS; COLLEGIUM PRACTICUM Generale & Speciale de Morbis Virorum, Mulierum & Infantium.
COLLEGIUM CHIRURGICUM.
Notæ in *Morelli* Methodum de formulis Medicamentorum præſcribendis; in *Ludovici* Diſſertationes Pharmaceuticas; & in *SCHROEDERI* Pharmacopœam.
Chymia Rationalis; cum Collegio Caſuali, & variis curioſiſque Diſſertationibus aliis.
OPUS POSTHUMUM,
Poſt varias Editiones mancas, nunc hinc inde ſuppletum, & Indice copioſiſſimo inſtructum. *Curâ*
D. GEORGII FRANCI,
In Electorali *Heidelberg.* Univerſit. Med. Prof. Primar. ac Pro-Cancellar. aliquot S. R. I. Electorum & Princip. Conſiliarii & Archiatri.

TOMUS I.

LONDINI,
Proſtant apud *Sam. Smith* ad inſignia Principis *Walliæ* in Cœmeterio Divi *Pauli.* 1688.

Fig. 18. *Floyer's copy of Michael Ettmüller,* Opera Omnia *(1688), the Library, The Queen's College, Oxford.*

Fig. 19. *David Sennert (1572-1637), frontispiece to his* Opera Omnia *(Leiden, 1666) that Floyer donated to the Library, The Queen's College, Oxford.*

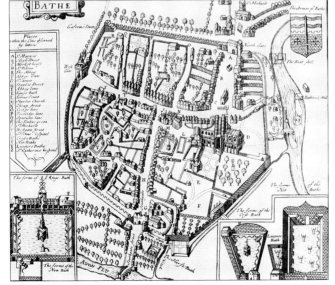

Fig. 20. *Illustrated map of Bath from Robert Peirce,* Bath Memoirs: or, Observations on Three and Forty Years Practice at the Bath *(1697).*

Any town of great trade is the fittest place to settle in. But no great estate can be got by country practice; 'tis very slavish and meanly rewarded. Never meddle with any studies which concern not the practice of physic, but read both the old and the new authors to be fully instructed in that art. Collect all the medicines you hear that have been successful, especially the method and form of giving simple medicines.[74]

Meddle not with any parties in church or state. Take your religion from your Bible and the history of the church in the first 300 years and the Nicene creed.[75] Never act against any laws of the land and heartily present nothing but your profession in physic without fraud or tricks.

Avoid all drinking company, the diversions and sports of the country and the assemblies of females, by which too much time is misspent from business and study. Choose of a society of men who are prudent, sober, learned and religious, and their examples of virtuous life imitate.

You will have sufficient evidence from the fabric of the body and circulation and the secretions of humours that there is a God that made it; and believe that he appointed you to the art of preserving that curious machine and to cure its defects. And that he has obliged you to be industrious, compassionate, charitable, humble, prudent in words and easy in conversation and, above all, to depend on the Creator of human bodies for your success in preserving its life and operation for the term he has appointed you to it.

Chapter 2

God is the Author of the Art of Physic

THE INVENTION of physic, as well as other useful arts, was imputed by the heathen to their gods, for which they deified them. Such was Apollo (Fig. 21), Aesculapius (Fig. 22), Isis [and] Osiris (Fig. 23), and they had their temples and sacrifices. But in the Ecclesiasticus 'tis said: *The Lord hath created the physician, and of the most high cometh healing.*(Ch.38, v.1)

Fig. 21. *Apollo from Daniel le Clerc,* Histoire de la Médecine *(1723).*

Fig. 22. *Aesculapius from Daniel le Clerc,* Histoire de la Médecine *(1723).*

Fig. 23. *Isis and Osiris from Daniel le Clerc,* Histoire de la Médecine *(1723).*

I will first consider the original of diseases and the virtues given to remedy and from thence show that God is the author of physic. Death and disease arose from the poison of the forbidden fruit and all we have from Adam is our bodies and their natural propensity to sensual pleasures and violent passions. All these are mechanical dispositions altered to wicked inclinations by the fruit of a venomous tree. And we may observe strange effects from venomous plants.

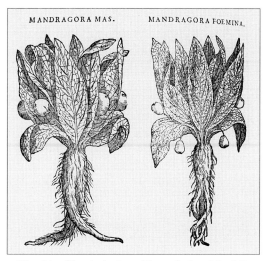

Fig. 24. *Mandrake from Pietro Andrea Mattioli,* Commentarii ... Dioscorides *(1569).*

Henbane produces a stupor and madness and braying like a mule. Morion is a species of mandrake which produces foolishness (Fig. 24).[76] Out of datura is a stramonium [from which] Bartolet makes his fantastic medicine for mad people, which put them into different extravagant fancies; and some such effect the forbidden fruit had on Adam and Eve in creating an imagination of their nakedness.[77] By this poison the crasis of their humours was corrupted and the tranquility of their minds disturbed and this in time produced diseases which end in the dissolution of our bodies. The effects of all poisons are: *oppressio spiritus, angores cordis, pulsus parvi, et venena agunt coagulando vel dissoluendo sanguinem* (constriction of breathing, cardiac pains and weak pulses; poisons act by coagulating and dissolving the blood). And from such depraved blood and spirits in Adam some propensity to those indispositions would descend to his posterity.

When Adam had sinned, he was drove out of paradise to cultivate the earth by hard labour and into an air more unhealthful in an uncultivated soil. And the fruits there were less mature and sweet, and though he did not die, yet his body decayed by natural means, viz: ill seasons, bad diet, passions, [and] a laborious life. Horror and remorse tormented his mind and the many troubles of an unhappy life created sorrow, anger and cares, and all enjoyments were unsatisfactory through fear of death. And he saw among his posterity, hatred, revenge, envy, covetousness, tyranny, and impiety and lust. From these inward disorders of the mind and the ill use of the non-natural causes, arose many diseases. But the flood further corrupted the air and made the earth less fruitful, and they made the lives of men much shorter afterwards and sooner reduced the body to dust again.

Many diseases now depend on ill air in unnatural seasons. Such are epidemical fevers and unnatural effervescences in catarrhs, fluxes, dysenteries and pestilential fevers. Our nourishment is oft corrupted by moist seasons or we use it intemperately. All parts of the earth's superficies are confused with stone, sand and minerals, by which its fertility is hindered and its waters are impregnated by pernicious salts and terrestrial particles. We now drink too much of fermented liquor, eat too much flesh and salt meats, unwholesome diet, corrupt waters and smutted corn, which has a putrid smell. They now cause some epidemical diseases (Fig. 25). And all our plants are too crude in cold wet summers.

Some diseases are consequents and punishments of unlawful pleasures, as the pox; or of luxury, as ill digestion, rheumatism, gout, stone, [and] dropsy. These are the common effects of passions: hysteric and hypochondriac cases and madness. Some infirmities are inflicted on men to restrict them from those vices they are inclined to, as [to] the want of sight, hearing, lameness, and most of those chronical diseases with which we are born, or befall us in our youths; or else they are designed for the trial of our patience.

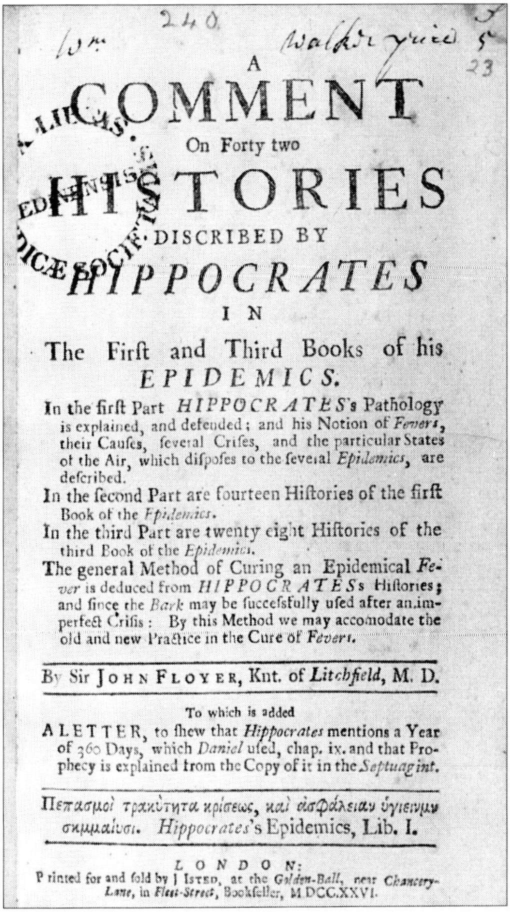
A
COMMENT
On Forty two
HISTORIES
DISCRIBED BY
HIPPOCRATES
IN
The First and Third Books of his
EPIDEMICS.

In the first Part *HIPPOCRATES*'s Pathology is explained, and defended; and his Notion of *Fevers*, their Causes, several Crises, and the particular States of the Air, which disposes to the several *Epidemics*, are described.

In the second Part are fourteen Histories of the first Book of the *Epidemics*.

In the third Part are twenty eight Histories of the third Book of the *Epidemics*.

The general Method of Curing an Epidemical *Fever* is deduced from *HIPPOCRATES*s Histories; and since the *Bark* may be successfully used after an imperfect Crisis: By this Method we may accomodate the old and new Practice in the Cure of *Fevers*.

By Sir JOHN FLOYER, Knt. of *Litchfield*, M. D.

To which is added
A LETTER, to shew that *Hippocrates* mentions a Year of 360 Days, which *Daniel* used, chap. ix. and that Prophecy is explained from the Copy of it in the *Septuagint*.

Πεπασμοὶ ταχυτῆτα κρίσεως, καὶ ἀσφάλειαν ὑγιεινὴν σημαίνουσι. *Hippocrates*'s Epidemics, Lib. I.

LONDON:
Printed for and sold by J. ISTED, at the *Golden-Ball*, near *Chancery-Lane*, in *Fleet-Street*, Bookseller, MDCCXXVI.

Fig. 25. *Title page of Floyer's* Comment *(1726) on Case Histories from Hippocrates's* Epidemics.

It was an ancient opinion amongst the Jews that many diseases do not come from common causes but are inflicted by evil spirits. By Satan's power Job had the leprosy; a woman in the Gospel was bound by Satan eighteen years under her infirmity; and St Paul's infirmity is called a messenger of Satan.[78] And madness and some extraordinary convulsions seem to us to come from the same hand. And they who were delivered over to Satan by the apostle were afflicted by diseases, so that we may believe his power is now restrained but may be permitted on just excommunications. And our present epidemical and pestilential diseases may be from thence since their causes are unknown to us.

It is probable that swine's flesh and that of many other animals, as well as leaven bread in constant use, were forbid the Jews because of hot bodies and hot countries, which made them subject to the leprosy. Our teas, coffee [and] sugar are used too much in our diet and in our soups. These over ferment our humours, accelerate our pulses and hasten old age.

We have no probable account of the original of our distempers but from the scripture. But they are inflicted on us for punishment of our sin, to torment us in a miserable life and at last to destroy our bodies. But man was at first designed to have been immortal and to have lived in a pleasant, and fruitful paradise. And he might have prevented all decay by eating of the tree of life; and there was no toil in Adam's employment and there he might have the favour of God's presence. The business God has allotted to physicians is the preventing or curing diseases or, at least, a palliative management of chronical infirmities by a proper diet, and to allay the pains and the grievous symptoms for some time.

Chirurgery and dietetics are the most ancient parts of physic, because wounds, tumours, ulcers, [and] inflammations did happen from the beginning, when man was turned out of paradise. And God himself by his angels brought famines, plague and the sword upon whole kingdoms to punish them for their idolatry and immoralities.

The next argument I shall use is that God has endowed our medicines with various [tastes] and smells and, by them, we know their virtues and cure diseases by contrary tastes; and this [is] a full proof that [He] is the author of physic. By our tastes and smells we discover the virtues of diet and medicines and then, by our reason and experience, we are taught to use contrary tastes to the diseased quality of our humour which produce any diseased action. And when we find any experiment agrees with our judgement by the sensible tastes we know the true method of correcting the cacochymias. And if we reason from the success of any taste we can conclude that the cacochymia had a contrary taste to that of our medicine. Since diseases happened to Adam before his death as well as

36

to his posterity, we must allow that he had the same sagacity the beasts have who, by their senses, discern those remedies which are useful to them.

Solomon's wisdom exceeded all that of the East and of Egypt and his knowledge in natural philosophy was part of his wisdom. All plants, beasts and trees and their virtues were known to him and their natural uses and all their wisdom were given him by God. He was older than all the Grecian authors of physic and from him the great improvements in physic were derived. From the scriptures we know that God prescribed some remedies for diseases, as washing for the leprosy and a poultice of figs for a plague sore; and he sent his angel into the pool of Bethesda.[79] Antoninus[80] affirms that Aesculapius prescribed cold bathing and diverse remedies to those who slept and dreamed in the temple.

We use many stimuli to irritate the motion of the solid parts, such as sternutatories, masticatories, vomitories, purges, pulti [sic], [and] blisters; and all these quicken the circulation of [the] humours. And we stop their violent motions by opiates which occasion a delirium in some and, in others, pleasant dreams, by which they divert the flux of spirits into the organ and that stops the circulation and secretions.

How many thousand lives have been preserved by the use of the bark given in proper circumstances?[81] And for that reason Mr Dryden calls it the bark of the tree of life. How many useful balsams and gums has America lent us, by which great cures may be done? Great varieties of vegetable, and animal and mineral products has chymistry afforded, in the form of spirits, salts and oils. We want not medicines to cure our diseases if given in due quantities and where they are indicated.

God has given us our senses whereby, with the help of experiments, we can discern the virtues of all our medicines. By their tastes and smells we know their qualities: of hot medicines which accelerate our circulations, and all the cold tastes [which] stop the vehemency of it and the secretions. And, by our senses, we can discern the natural and [the] preternatural state of humours, which are the antecedent causes of our diseases. And from particular observations of ours, we make general rules.

In the age before the flood, mankind lived long and they might well observe that by due exercise, wholesome diet and governing their passions, their lives were prolonged; and, by idleness, ill diet and ingovernable passions, they were shortened. And by these reflections they began a right use of such things and, by long experience, they learned the benefit of temperance and industry and, by these observations and the use of hot and cold bathing, they cured or prevented diseases. All the ancient experiments were at last collected into an art by Hippocrates and Galen who, by a long experience, described all diseases, their causes, symptoms, cures and prognostics. I will next observe that all our success in practice depends on God. I hope it cannot be thought impertinent in a physical discourse to mention God in it.

Since Hippocrates observed that the knowledge of the gods belongs to physic, since much is attributed to them in that profession. And Galen observes that God is invoked by hymns [and] adored, loved and worshipped in a pure mind, [and] that there is one chief prince of the gods, the best and [the] greatest. And He knows our thoughts, He made the world and our bodies, and formed the foetus; and knows whether it be an animal that is first in the womb and what part is made first. He observes that nature is wise [and] just and provides for all creatures and is artificious (subtle).

Physicians are but second instrumental causes who, out of [a] multitude of remedies, must choose the most effectual and use it in due time and then depend on God for his success. God gives success to ordinary means with a design to baffle the confident and proud boasts of arcanas and panaceas. This gives the modest practiser the reputation of being fortunate and an extraordinary success establishes his reputation against his envious competitors. When the physician has a true sense of religion, his virtuous patient will believe that God will more readily give him his blessing, than to the profane practiser. The physician's religion obliges him to charity, compassion [and] the despising of vain glory and riches; all which are acceptable to God and these please all pious patients. And they securely confide in their doctor who practises not only for fees, but as an agent employed by providence to perform his cure safely and speedily.

Every person is obliged to perform some service to the public society of men, for whose peace, plenty and health, all are engaged to promote. The soldier defends our property from foreign enemies, the tradesman provides useful goods for others, the divine instructs the ignorant, and the lawyer defends the estate. So physicians are obliged to cure the sick. The end of human employment is to serve God's providence and promote the common conveniences in all societies; and, for a conscientious discharge of our several employments, we shall receive a reward in the next state, and a comfortable reflection in this life.

No person can expect the cure of all diseases by physic, because diseases will [at] last end in death. A physician will have performed his duty if he cures, in many persons, diseases such as pains, inflammations, fevers, obstructions and fluxes. In the Ecclesiasticus 'tis said: *That he shall [also] pray to the Lord, and he shall prosper that which they give for ease and remedy [to prolong life]* (Ch.38, v.14). Hence we learn that the physician must pray for success and expect God's blessing in due time. For all success is uncertain and therefore it must be prayed for and thanks must be given for it. And these are the reasons of its uncertainty:

38

1. The study of physic is long and life is short.
2. The judgement of the cause of diseases is difficult and many are symptomatical and not primary.
3. The proper occasions and opportunities of cure escape through the neglect of the diseases at first, in their beginning.
4. Experiments are deceitful for want of nice observations of the circumstances on which experience is grounded.
5. The patients or attendants do not play their parts; through fear or obstinancy they neglect the advice given.

'Tis a kind providence which directs the physician's attention and judgement, and appoints the proper time for cure, and excites the patient to a due care of themselves.

I may further observe that God orders an honour to be given to the physician: Ecclesiasticus (Ch.38, vv.1-4): *Honour the physician with the honour due to him; and he shall receive [the] honour of the king; and the skill of the physician shall lift up his head, and in the sight of great men he shall be in admiration; they that are wise will not abhor them.* The honour is procured by success in curing great men who value their lives most; and the vulgar also admire great events, which are rare. To all, the physician is useful, by easing pains, restoring them to the pleasures of life, and delivering them from the present fears of death. And who will not admire that skill which discerns diseases by the pulse, and foretells the future events of it; and can discover many past accidents belonging to it, without any information?

Those medicines are very much admired which can extinguish the fury of fevers, stop violent evacuations and allay the acute torments by desired sleep; and those which to the vulgar seem unlikely to cure, as cold baths.

My last observation shall be that God usually determines, by some second causes, every man to some particular employment or profession. He requires some public service of every person, as soon as he attains to a mature age: that he either employ his body or mind to serve some end of providence. And, if we do some useful service to the public or our neighbour, we thereby serve God and shall receive a reward in this life or the next for employing our talent well. 'Tis said that Galen's father had an admonition in a dream to breed his son a physician.[82] And Hippocrates learnt his physic from his father and in his time it was confined to particular families.[83] And 'tis usual that the fame of the skill of any person in a family will incline some of their posterity to the same studies.

We seem to ourselves to choose our employments and to think of nothing more than a way of living and getting money for the subsistence of our family. But, if we nicely reflect on all [our] circumstances, our education, company, studies of natural philosophy, as well as our inclination and natural capacities, and the means by which providence determined us to undertake the profession of physic to cure diseased bodies. And for that end, [providence] has given some men particular qualifications and natural propensity to that employment.[84] Law requires a good memory, great assurance, and volubility of tongue and the art of logic and a contentious humour, [and] of arguing upon all occasions. The study of physic requires a delight in making many experiments in natural philosophy, a curiosity in dissection of bodies and, at last, great industry in application of medicines with a charitable design of serving our neighbour. All these are the work of a lively imagination and a moderate degree of judgement and memory. And in these natural endowments consist our natural disposition to physic, and these are given us by God. A good memory disposes us for attaining Greek and Latin languages in which physic was writ by the compilers of that art. A clear judgement helps physicians to reason well about the different causes of the diseases and the indications for cure. A lively imagination invents many experiments and observes the minutest circumstances in practice. The various dispositions of memory, judgement and imagination, gives them their several inclinations to the arts and trades, and some of the faculties mentioned are more necessary in one than the other. And this difference of intellectual faculties is from God, who thereby determines every man's employment, as he does his sex, the time of his birth, and the age he must live in, and that particular scene of affairs in which he must act his part. All these things depend on God's providence or decrees, so riches and all external blessings depend on his pleasure.

Some hypochondriacs divert themselves with chymistry, anatomy [and] botany. And such studies easily lead men into the study of physic, which is the most useful end of those studies. Many young men have ill health, some infirmities in their senses or viscera and that determines them to the study of physic that they may cure themselves as well as others. But such physicians cannot thoroughly pursue that long study, nor are capable of undergoing the severe fatigue required in the practice of physic. Therefore, in their latter days, they write more than others, who can bear the drudgery of long practice. And, when they can practice no longer, then let them write an exact history of their own diseases and its symptoms, and note the methods and medicines which they have found most effectual by their own practice or in the old and modern authors, that we serve posterity by our improvements of our profession.

Chapter 3

Concerning the Physician's Industry in the Study of Physic and those Arts which are Useful and the Method of Obtaining a Perfect Knowledge in his Art

ALL THE MORAL virtues ought to attend the practice of physic. And these are to be learnt from our Bible, as well as the old heathen morality. By these the physician will become ισοθεοσ (equal with God), as well as by his philosophy and learning. I will first mention his industrious pursuits of the several arts necessary in the practice of physic, and not to undertake any cures till he has run through a long study, and has acquired that κοισις (judgement), which Hippocrates requires in a physician.

We must come to the study well instructed in the learned languages in which Hippocrates and Galen have writ. And the Latin language is as necessary as the Greek, [Latin being the language] in which the modern have writ their books. The physician's reason ought to be improved by logical definitions, and distinctions and disputations. Galen was very expert in this art and wrote some books about it.[85] Hippocrates in his letter to his son Thessalus recommends the study of geometry and arithmetic.[86] He says the first will clear the understanding and, by its figures and demonstrations, teach us the figures and motions of the bones and muscles; and arithmetic he thought necessary for reckoning the critical days and the doses of medicines.[87] And that we find [arithmetic] is necessary in the physiologia and mechanical motions of the fluids, their quantities and their evacuations, and proportion of the viscera to one another, or their whole weight.

Both Hippocrates and Galen believed astronomy useful in the education of a physician, because 'tis necessary to know the changes of the seasons and the motion of the sun and moon to which they attributed the change of diseases.[88] Galen was an admirer of rhetoric, music and poetry, ethics, history, grammar, [and] metaphysics. All these may be ornaments to physicians and may procure him esteem, but [are] not necessary to the art of physic. Rhetoric may be useful to comfort the melancholic and to encourage the fearful, to appease the angry and furious and to persuade the obstinate to the use of medicines. Ethics are useful to the physician for governing both his own and patients' passions, which are the causes of diseases in the hypochondriac and hysteric.

This is the glorious character of Galen: he had Chrysippus's dialectics,[89] Aristotle's philosophy, Plato's theology, Euclid's geometry (Fig. 26), Ptolemy's astronomy, Pythagoras's music,[90] Demosthenes' eloquence,[91] Homer's poetry and Hippocrates's physic.

The most useful of all sciences is natural philosophy[92] and anatomy for the institution of a physician; and the knowledge of plants is part of it.

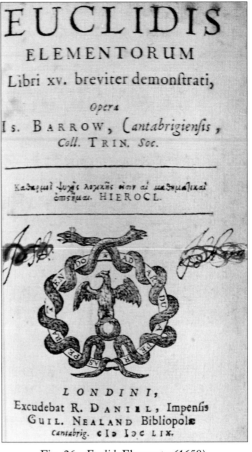

Fig. 26. *Euclid*, Elements *(1659)*.

Anatomy shows us the natural and preternatural state of the fluids and solid parts. Botany and chymistry discover the nature of our medicines by their sensible qualities. Natural philosophy discovers the immediate principles which compose our humours, and the several causes of their alterations and the effects of the external causes on our bodies. Though all these sciences may be in some degree of advantage to the institution in physic,[93] yet many errors have sprung from the introduction of too much of them into the tracts of physic.

The old Aristotelian philosophy introduced their elements into physic to explain the humours and diseases; and thence came the four intemperies, the hot, cold, dry and moist, whereas there are as many

42

intemperies as there are varieties of preternatural tastes in the humours, viz. acid, acrid, salt, bitter, corrosive [and] putrid, which the ancients imputed to choler and its different mixtures. And these are the cold intemperies: the slimey, watery, and acerb tastes, which are the preternatural pituitas of the Aristotelians. They explained all things by the quality of the elements, whereas no more was necessary than the sensible tastes and qualities of humours, and their secretion in too great quantity, or their deficiency by obstructions or ill digestions; or the violent motion of humours which we know by the great frequent and quick pulses; by this we know the hot cacochymias and, by a slow, small and rare pulse, the cold cacochymias.

The Aristotelians looked no further than the tactile qualities of the body. By the hot and cold, they judged of the qualities of our humours and, by the dryness and moisture, of the quantities of them. Their meaning we may now explain by a better philosophy and a more exact anatomy, by which we improved our explications and made all their long discourses from the elements unuseful.

The *prisca medicina* of Hippocrates taught us to enquire into the nature of our humours by their tastes, and that diseases are to be imputed to preternatural tastes. By this method physic would have been better improved, but the Galenists followed Aristotle's philosophy too much. And, from their mistakes, we may in this age observe that 'tis a dangerous error to establish the practice of physic on any general notion of philosophy. We ought rather to adhere to the observation of our senses. Neither has the new philosophy of Cartesius or Epicurus made any improvement in physic, because 'tis impossible to know the figures and motions of particles; nor none of their attraction can now be proved.[94] 'Tis not necessary to recourse to remote principles for the explaining of our diseases. The preternatural qualities are all sensible, or may be made so by some experiments. And if we know the disease, we find its symptoms depend on it. The external causes are subject to our senses, and the antecedent cause appears in the great or small pulses by which the qualities of the blood are discovered; and medicines of a contrary taste to the cause of the disease must be applied to cure it.

The causes of a disease are usually some alteration in the solid or fluid parts. But we are not yet fully informed of the nice composition of one fibre and the causes of its motion; nor do we know the composition of one globule in the fluids and how the water, the slimy fibres, the oily and the salt, are mixed in it; nor where they are separated from each globule by the secretions.

Chymistry can show us some sensible products about the nature of the principles of vegetables. We taste the acid in cream of tartar. Their oils are very evident in chymical oils, their earths in ashes and lixivial salts and their water in distilled waters. But these produce different mixtures and qualities in the juices of plants. And chymistry shows us how many products may be made from an animal body by fire: water, a volatile salt and an oil, and ashes, appear after their distillation. But these principles have a different state in the mixture of humours so that, because we distil these principles, we cannot conclude they are the natural principles of our blood, in which we observe a serum, a salt acid in it, a vitriolic taste, [and] a fibrous or glutinous part; and an oiliness in the omentum and gall bladder. 'Tis an error in chymistry to explain animal humours by chymical principles and to impute all diseases to an alkali and acid, which our senses cannot observe in diseases. Why should we call our animal oils sulphur [and] the spirits or salts, mercury? The principles of animals differ from minerals as much as their substances do and this change of names makes some mistakes in believing their effects alike. Chymistry has found out some useful medicines, both in minerals and animals, but fewer in vegetables which the fire corrupts.

Chymists have brought an unjust contempt on the rational practice of physic by the non naturals and simple medicines. No sect has writ more nonsense about the nature of humours and the virtues of their medicines. They are general[ly] ignorant in anatomy, botany and in a general philosophy.

Since the causes of diseases are from their quantity or defect, or their sensible qualities altered, and their too quick motion or too slow through the solid pipes which contain them, so much of [the] mechanical learning as is necessary to measure the motion of them, and the capacity of their vessels may be sound advantage in anatomical tracts. But that will never improve the practice of physic. For, if we know the degrees of circulation of the pulse, that is sufficient for the knowledge of diseases and their causes which depend on motion; and the different secretions manifest the quality of our humours.

Many diseases depend on the solids and those are like the faults in a water engine. The vessels are compressed, obstructed, broke or leaky. Acrids prick, irritate and convulse the solid parts in pains and convulsions. We find aneurysms in the arteries, varices in the veins and hydatids in the lymphatics. The fibres may be too large or tense. In children they are lax, soft [and] flexible, but [they] grow hard and drier in men, and in the old age, most hard, dry or callous, or wrinkled or varicose by wine, cares [and] hard labour. We make the solids lax and flexible by baths, hot lotions, fomentations [and] unctions which have been of late too much disused. We make the fibres more tense by friction, exercise, ustion [and] cold baths.

In fevers and hot constitutions, the fibres are irritated to a greater tension which is relieved by bleeding, and water drinking and cool emulsions. All crudity of our humours produces a laxity in the fibres and then we make them more tense by bitters, steel, lixivial salts [and] aromatic styptics. In all obstructions in hot constitutions, the tensity of the fibres must be helped by bleeding, baths, lotions of the feet, emollient lotions [and] oils. These relax the convulsions of the fibres which obstruct secretions.

The oscillatory motions of the fibres not being sensible, we can take no indications thence. But, when the pulse is great and frequent then their tension and motion is greatest, and more lax and weak when the pulse is small and rare. Therefore, by the pulse we know the tension and laxity, and these indispositions only indicate topical medicines to alter them. And, since the hot intemperies make the tension, all the topics must be water, slimy [and] acid styptic; and the topics in the cold intemperies must be the hot tastes, bitters, acrids, aromatics, foetids [and] convulsives. The same tastes as will correct the humours inwardly must be used as topics outwardly.

In pleurisies and pains the extreme irritation stops the motion of the blood and all secretions. And the same irritation is [present] in colics and the stone, and this stop produces inflammations and obstructions. Vomits, purges, diaphoretics, and diuretics, and all deobstruent medicines are the inward stimuli; the outward are blisters, cuppings, friction, sinapisms, hot cataplasms, baths, cauteries, burning [and] acupunctures.[95] Sometimes the fibres in hot constitutions are too sensible and require opiates.

Too much laxity of the solids in children and old men hinders the circulation of humours and occasions catarrhs, want of appetite or looseness. And, in the flesh, a laxity produces a nervous consumption; and this is to be cured by bitters and steel, antiscorbutics and cephalics, and not by milk. The lienteria is a laxity of the pylorus; epiphora is a laxity of the glandules of the eye and requires styptics; an ischuria is a laxity of the glands of the kidneys; and a diabetes [is] the laxity of the lymphatics and requires styptics of *terra Japonica*. In sleep the fibres are relaxed and that causes sweats. In palsy there is a laxity of the fibres. And the sphincter of the bladder is too lax in incontinence of urine. The obstruction of the mesentery from lax glands may [be] cured by coffee and mastication of cinnamon. Dropsies [are] from the laxity of fibres. Continual pains in the gout make a laxity and luxation of the joints. Deafness is from the laxity of the tympanum; from the laxity of the retina, blindness; the loss of taste and smell, from the laxity of those nerves; and an impotency to venery, from a laxity; a gonorrhoea from the laxity of the seminal vessels; fluor albus from the laxity of the vagina; luxation from the laxity of the fibres, too much fat from the laxity of the fat vessels; the procidence of the uterus or anus; consumptions from the laxity of the lungs; nausea and vomiting from the laxity of the mouth of the stomach. A laxity in the bladder produces the stone. In children who cannot correct the viscosity there bred, the rickets [is] from a laxity of the muscular fibres; [and] haemorrhages from laxity in the lungs and the blood vessels.

I have transcribed this from Baglivius to show how much we must respect the solids, as well as the fluids in our practice.[96] But we must consider, as the solids force the circulation and by that digest, sanguify and produce the secretions, a violent circulation produces all the hot cacochymias, and a too slow, the cold ones. From these observations which we know by the pulses, we have this general indication, that we must stop the violent, and accelerate the slow circulation (or, according to the new name, oscillation). A diet of hot tastes, hot air, hot baths, much labour, hot passions [and] vigilia, stopping secretions, raise the circulation and quicken it. But the cool tastes in our diet, cold air, cold baths, idleness, the cooler passions, as fear, sadness, much sleep, and all evacuations that are natural, stop the violent circulation and pulses. But, besides this general indication, we must use some for abating the quantity, and altering the quality of our cacochymias, though these faults are the products of the general circulation. Yet, so long as the cacochymia continues, that will stimulate if hot; or if cold, stop the circulation; and it cannot become moderate that is corrected and evacuated. The pleurisy has a pain and constriction on the part of the pleura occasioned by sizy blood and, besides that there is a fever. For the ebullition and siziness, we bleed, and use cool diet, and cooling medicines and some sudorifics; for the irritation and contraction of the solids, oils and emollients. Therefore in the cure of all diseases let us take the proper indications, both from the solids and fluids. Though the solids give the general circulation, yet the fluids regulate that motion according to their heat and stimulating qualities, that is vehement or slow. And when we correct the hot humours, we thereby abate the tension of the solids. For, by the instance, in a pleurisy we find that the siziness produces the tension and contraction in the solids and that is the product or effect of the fluids. But sometimes the solids, by external irritation, corrupt the fluid by stagnations, evacuations, tumours [and] inflammations. And the indications are most safely taken from both.

Since some diseases are primarily in the solids or fluids, we must describe them and their symptoms by their true causes which are the original causes of the diseases, whether the solid or fluid or both; and always note the pathognomonic symptoms. But we must also note all the cases in which a disease is only a symptom, because that cannot be cured entirely without respect to the primary disease. And in treating of any disease we must describe all the causes of it and, whether primary or symptomatical we must distinguish them.

Acute diseases require our enquiry into the external or internal cause of them. If the fever runs too high we must depress it by cool medicines; if it runs too low we must raise the fever by hot medicines and permit the ebullition or fermentation to run to its crisis. In this consists the cure of fevers. But in chronical diseases we must know the causes by dissection, as is related in Bonetus's *Sepulchretum* (Fig. 27),[97] whether [the] inflammations, schirrhus, gangrenes, impostumes, or smaller obstructions of the viscera, or extravasations of the humours, blood, or serum, or inflations of the nerves or rupture of membranes, or gangrenes, [or] cancers which produce these diseases.

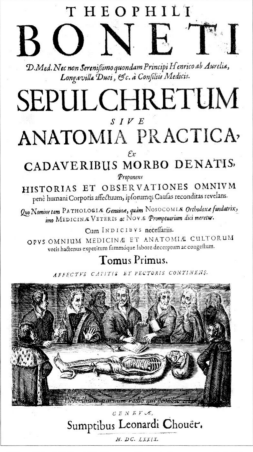

Fig. 27. *Théophile Bonet*, Sepulchretum *(1679)*.

47

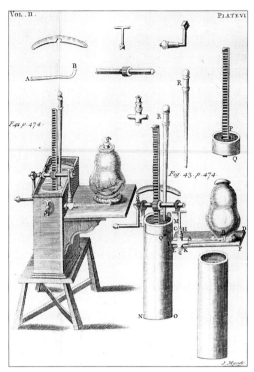

F.42 p. 474.

Fig. 43. p. 474.

J. Mynde.

Fig. 28. *Air-pump, from Peter Shaw,* Philosophical Works of Robert Boyle *(1738).*

This is the scheme a young student will find useful in his study.

The first year, to study Mr Boyle's books (Fig. 28), and see those experiments which are usually taught in a course of natural philosophy;[98] and, in the afternoons, to see a course of chymistry, and read Mr Lemery's *Chymistry* (Fig. 29).

The second year, to see a course of anatomy, and to observe the natural tastes of the blood and all its secretions; and, in the afternoon, to visit the physic garden and to taste all the plants used in physic and to range them under their tastes: the mucilaginous, the acid, the styptic, the sweet, [the] oily, the bitter, the acrid, the aromatic, the foetid and [the] corrosive classes. And it will be necessary to observe all the mixtures of tastes, but chiefly the prevailing tastes by which they are reduced into classes.

In the third year, 'tis convenient to begin the study of the theory of physic writ by Riverius, who comprehends all the old logical theory and terms; and, in the afternoons, to read his practice and Dr Willis's *Pharmaceutic* and other books in this method.[99]

The first disease is fever and effervescences. The most useful book is Dr Morton's in the continued, intermittent and malignant and infectious fevers and the plague.

The second disease is inflammations and these may be all read together: pleuritis, peri-pneumonia, rheumatismus, sciatica, lumbago, [illegible], angina, aphtha, parotis, nephritis, colica biliosa, [and] inflammations of the liver.

The third disease is the evacuations by vomits, diarrhoeas, urine, sweat, gonorrhoea, fluor albus [and] coughs.

The fourth disease is the haemorrhages: at the nose, spitting blood, pissing [blood], vomiting blood, flux of the menses, lochia, abortions, [and] flux of the haemorrhoids.

The fifth disease is obstruction of the viscera: liver in the jaundice, spleen in hypochondriacs, lympha in the scrofula (Fig. 30), [and] lacteals in the tumour of the belly.

The sixth is the suppression of the natural forces: the urine is suppressed in ischuria, the stools in the obstructio alvi, the sweat in transpiration stopped, or the menses are stopped, or lochia, or the haemorrhoids.

The seventh is the evacuation of the serum, into the cavities: in that of the belly, ascites; in the breast and scrotum, anasarca in the flesh; tympany in the omentum, or betwixt the peritoneum and muscles of the belly or uterus.

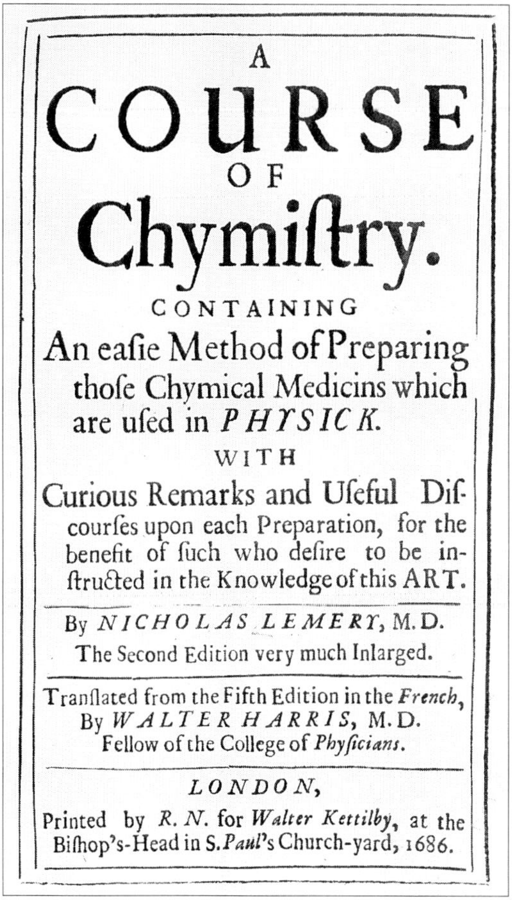

A

COURSE

OF

Chymiſtry.

CONTAINING

An eaſie Method of Preparing thoſe Chymical Medicins which are uſed in *PHYSICK*.

WITH

Curious Remarks and Uſeful Diſcourſes upon each Preparation, for the benefit of ſuch who deſire to be inſtruĉted in the Knowledge of this ART.

By *NICHOLAS LEMERY*, M.D.
The Second Edition very much Inlarged.

Tranſlated from the Fifth Edition in the *French*,
By *WALTER HARRIS*, M.D.
Fellow of the College of *Phyſicians*.

LONDON,

Printed by *R. N.* for *Walter Kettilby*, at the Biſhop's-Head in S. *Paul*'s Church-yard, 1686.

Fig. 29. *Nicholas Lemery*, A Course of Chymistry (1686).

The eighth are the diseases of the animal spirits oppressed in the apoplexy, palsy [and] lethargy.

The ninth [is] from [the] too great rarefaction of the spirits: delirium, mania [and] vigilia; and in pains, cephalalgia, cardialgia, colia, otalgia, odontalgia, calculus, podagra [and] arthritis vaga.

The tenth [are] these diseases which depend on the circulatory organs: asthma on the lungs; tremor from the heart oppressed; and syncopy,

49

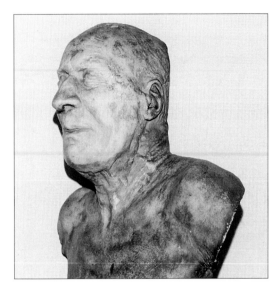

Fig. 30. *Scarring from childhood scrofula evident in the Death Mask of Dr Samuel Johnson.*

hysteric and hypochondriac affections in the inflation of the diaphragm; and convulsion.

This is the short method of study of physic, because all fevers are from an ebullition of the blood and known by a quick and frequent pulse. Inflammations are from sizy blood and have a great and hard pulse. The evacuations are from acrid humours, and the pulse is less but frequent. Haemorrhages have a great soft pulse. Obstructions have a great viscidity or sliminess in the humours and, if viscid, the pulse is hard, if pituitous, soft. The suppression of the natural evacuations have a great and high pulse, and depend on viscidity or pituitous humours. The evacuation of the serum has a small quick pulse. The rest of the pulse I have transcribed in the second part of my advice to young students. And there is a perfect scheme of the tastes of vegetable, animal, and mineral medicines and of the pulses in every disease. And the causes of each pulse which show antecedent cacochymias in each disease are described in *The Pulse-Watch*.

In the fourth year, 'tis necessary to go to the hospitals in London, Holland, Paris or Italy, and there to learn the practice in chyurgery and to collect the most effectual medicines in every disease and the vulgar methods of practice (Fig. 31).

As to medicines, there are forms enough in our dispensatories: in Bate, Fuller, Quincy,[100] [and in] Mr Boyle's *Receipts* (Fig. 32).[101] But there

Fig. 31. *St Caecilia's Hospital where bedside teaching was conducted in Leiden.*

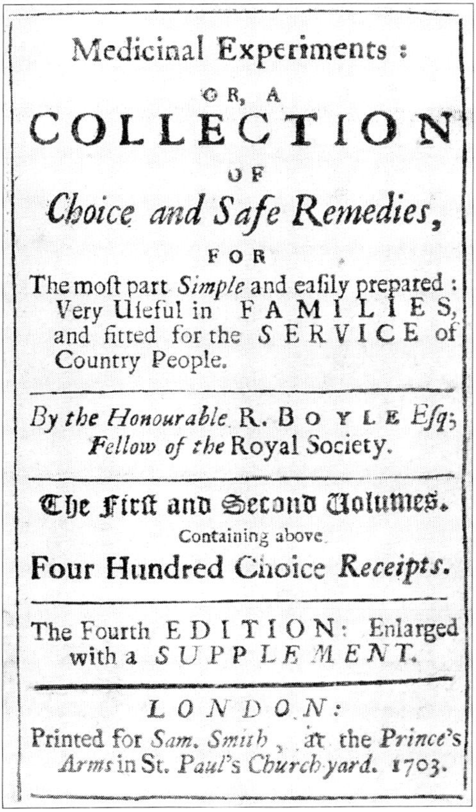

Medicinal Experiments :

ᴼᴿ, ᴬ

COLLECTION

ᴼᶠ

Choice and Safe Remedies,

ᶠ ᴼ ᴿ

The moſt part *Simple* and eaſily prepared : Very Uſeful in F A M I L I E S, and fitted for the S E R V I C E of Country People.

By *the Honourable* R. B o ʏ ʟ ᴇ *Eſq;* *Fellow of the* Royal Society.

The Firſt and Second Volumes.
Containing above

Four Hundred Choice Receipts.

The Fourth E D I T I O N : Enlarged with a S U P P L E M E N T.

L O N D O N :
Printed for *Sam. Smith*, at the *Prince's* *Arms* in St. *Paul's Church yard.* 1703.

Fig. 32. *Robert Boyle,* Medicinal Experiments *(1703).*

51

wants the choice made out of them and those classed under their physical tastes by which the disease will be cured. And in every disease there ought to be different methods pointed out suitable to the hot or cold constitution, which require a distinction.

Ettmüller's *Practice* will furnish us with the new notion in each disease. But the old observations of the diagnostics, prognostics, and method of cure are never to be despised but revived and improved. Dioscorides[102] gives the best account of the tastes and virtues of plants and, amongst our new writers, Mr Ray's *History of Plants*[103] (Fig. 33), and Pomet (Fig. 34).[104] Galen was a great traveller through the choice cities of Asia and Syria, Alexandria, Egypt, Greece [and] Rome. And in England foreign physicians are more esteemed than our own natives by the vulgar.

Though some physicians may value themselves for poetry, languages, travels, curiosities in anatomy, and botany, and chymistry or philosophy, all wise men will think these nice studies impertinent to the cure of diseases for which end they ask the physician's advice. And 'tis certain that the more time has been spent on those studies, the less has been employed in the study and practice of physic. But those arts may be admired by those that are in health, but nothing will be acceptable to the sick but a judicious and rational method of practice by experienced medicines. This will procure a good success and that will support the reputation of the doctor and his art.

Fig. 33. *An Allegory of Gardening from John Ray,* Methodus Plantarum Nova *(1682).*

52

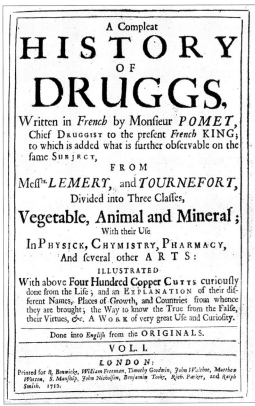

Fig. 34. *Pierre Pomet*, A Compleat History of
Druggs *(1712).*

All pretenders to universal medicines meet in time with ill success; their medicines are found to be cheats and disused. For, since diseases arise both from the hot and cold cacochymias, one medicine cannot be suitable to two contrary diseases. They, like Paracelsus, die young to the disgrace of their infallible medicine, whereas Hippocrates lived near to [a] hundred years by his art of preserving health.[105] Multitudes of the clinical arcanas as well as the old galenical antidotes which have had extravagant commendations by their authors are now disused. And a new medicine is always esteemed by the vulgar till, by many experiments, 'tis found unuseful. Whosoever considers the art necessary for the study of a physician and that he must use a long experience in that art to acquire any judgement in it, he will admire the industry of such a person. And by making a great progression in it he makes himself useful under God's providence, as well as serviceable to his neighbour. For God does not miraculously cure, but uses the physician as his instrument. We may observe Hippocrates' industry in collecting the history of epidemic fevers and [in] composing his aphorisms. Galen's anatomy, and his art of feeling the pulse, and his art of preserving health, and his large comment on Hippocrates, are sufficient instances of his indefatiguable industry. These examples we ought to imitate.

Physic had been long in Egypt before Hippocrates had reduced it into an art in Ezra's days, and the Egyptians might derive their tradition from the Jews.[106] The learned languages in Galen's time were the Persian and Ethiopic, where most of the Jews were driven; and 'tis probable that the Jews knew some tradition of natural philosophy from Solomon.

When the young physician has seen the practice in the different species of diseases, then he may read Hippocrates and Galen and any old author, and then he will be able to induce [i.e., discern from] both of the old and new writers what is most useful and most true. Therefore read the old authors as practice directs, but at first let the young student write down all the history and symptoms and consider the causes of them, and set down the indications and medicines, and keep a journal of his practice for some time which will make him very exact.

We must esteem all opinion without experience and practice [as] dangerous.[107] What is founded on experience is useful and instructive. But in obscure cases we only conjecture and, in such cases, we must preserve the opinion of the experienced persons.

When we hear the history of any case we may know the disease best by the first symptoms and the prognosis of it by those symptoms which succeed. And by argu[ing] from the cause of each symptom we come to the knowledge of the antecedent cause of the disease. And in fevers the blood commonly circulates too fast and the secretions are bilious or impregnate with a volatile urinous saltness. But in chronical disease the tartar, acid, serous and slimy humours abound and these are produced by a slow circulation. And from these two states we take the first indication, and the first step towards a cure is removing all the external causes which occasion the cacochymia.

Many diseases depend on the affections of the mind.[108] Sadness destroys the digestion and appetite [and] produces malignant fevers; anger occasions the flux of the menstrua, fevers and biliose diarrhoeas. In hypochondria and hysteric passions we cure by proper exercises: travails [travels], hunting, riding and the use of tepid baths. For women, music, dancing [and] conversation must be prescribed, as well as bathing and riding in the coach or on horseback in the country air. Patience, fortitude, prudence and a tranquility of mind must be recommended. The physician must promise great success but use all gentle means. But, in disease of anger, we must use all the cool regimen against the phrensy.

The physician ought to observe how one distemper changes into another by the circulation tending to another part and carrying the morbific matter thither. So a phthisis ends in a diarrhoea or sweats, and such successions are usually mortal because the patient was weakened by the first disease. A pleurisy is oft changed into a peripneumonia or phrenitis and that, or a lethargy, discharges by the jugular a purulent matter into the lungs and is fatal. To a dysentery a tenesmus succeeds, or lientery and a dropsy succeeds that. Great heat follows a feverish rigor, and a convulsion the wound of nerves; in wounds of the head, vomiting. And the omentum falling out putrifies; and blood in the wounds of the breast there putrifies if not let forth. The phrenitis, pleuritis and pulmonia are all cured alike, being inflammations from sizy blood which is oft drove by the circulation from one part into another. The melancholy is changed into an epilepsy and, a contra, the same being an acrid acid drove up on the nerves. The corrosive and sizy humours in a dysentery are sometimes conveyed into the hips, legs [and] stones, and discharges a purulent matter there. The pains in the stomach are oft succeeded by the gout and the gout by dysentery, which cures many great diseases. A dysentery too soon stopped ends in abscesses of the viscera or limbs. After haemoptoe, a phthysis and impostumation: these depend on the same cause, a tubercle in the lungs and that also produces the cough. Obstruction of the viscera breaks the lymphatics and occasions dropsies. All diseases are more dangerous which succeed others and most so when they relapse to the original again. So to a lethargy, a peripneumonia and a vomica succeed, and to a peripneumonia a lethargy is fatal.

A quartan cures an epilepsy, a diarrhoea an ophthalmy, a tertian a catarrh, and a fever a convulsion. The diarrhoea is cured by a vomit; these evacuate the morbific matter transferred to some secretory part. The sciatica and deafness oft succeed one another, both from sizy humours. So quinsies circulate down the jugulars into a peripneumonia. Some neighbouring parts communicate with one another, [as] the diseases of the spleen and liver. Diseases, by sympathy, ease the original, as vomiting the nephritis. Diseases of the head are communicated to the stomach by the nerves; those of the limbs return on the lungs by the vena cava.

A good crisis has sweats with a sleep after it and all symptoms become more easy. But, since our air is thicker and diet more gross than in Greece, we cannot have the same critical days in England. Therefore more time must be allowed for the depuration and secretions: our 9th rather than their 7th, our 17th rather than their 14th, our 21st rather than their 17th. We may probably allow 4 days more than they observed. And some such crises appear in our northern plagues, the measles and smallpox. This yet wants a further observation both in acute and some chronical cases, as the gout, rheumatisms [and] cough.

Nephritis transfers its abscesses to the loins. Madness ends in fatal convulsions. There is a sympathy between the breasts and uterus; the blood or serum is communicated by the veins from one to the other. Pains in the hypochondria oft end in cancers, all which depend on putrid, stagnating blood. The quartan ends in rheumatisms or ulcers in the skin, and the obstruction of the spleen produces quartans. The dropsy after acute diseases is fatal because they produce tumours in the viscera. If the humours transferred are evacuated they cure a disease but, if not evacuated, they increase it as the pain of the head on the quinsy, or delirium on a pleurisy. But a pleurisy cures a pulmonia, [and] a pleuritis a lethargy. The jaundice is often changed into a tympanitis, especially if there be calculose concretions in the bile bladder. Continued fevers are produced by hot medicines in the intermittents. The gout oft ends in the dropsy or asthma, but these are curable because they only depend on the want of a good circulation in the gouty. The convulsive asthma ends in the tympany, both being the effect of the inflation of the nervous fibres. The *mola convulsiva uteri* depends on the convulsive colic: and they have all the same cure, the evacuation of the irritating humours and the lenifying the irritated fibres, by unctions and baths.

In distempers of the brain, the circulation through it is altered by the violent contractions of the dura mater: in madness, vigilia, pains, epilepsies and convulsions. And the motion is too slow in coldness, torpors, melancholy; or oppressed in vertigos, apoplexy, palsy; or irregularly moved in passions. Since the whole substance of the brain is shaken or compressed by its systole and diastole and, since the dura mater communicates with the external membranes on the brain, we must always apply topical medicines to the head to accelerate the motion by plaisters and fomentations, or retard it by shaving and washing it with cold water or opiate unctions. As well as must correct the cacochymias which irritate or stop the systole of the membranes, that is observed to beat at the same moment as the heart does. Therefore the same cacochymias affect the heart and [the] brain alike. But, as the heart may have particular irritations by inflammation, tumours, or polypus, so may the membranes be affected originally by tumours, abscesses, polypus [or] varices, and be oppressed by extravasate[d] blood or lympha. The solid parts propel the fluids and the fluids act on the solids and both must be respected in the cure of cephalic diseases. The motion of the dura menix is from the nerves and arteries and they stimulate the fibres and lacerti in it to contraction. A fomentation of warm water to the feet, hands [or] belly relieves a delirium by drawing the circulation downwards. There is the same systole and diastole in the vena porta as in the sinus of the brain; both help the return of blood to the heart. But, in obstruction of those motions, I have observed a great pulsation in the hypochondria and these will require proper topics.

It would not be difficult to institute a college of physicians in Oxford by appointing one of the halls by an Act of Parliament for that profession only. And, by the consent of the several colleges, the physicians who are on their foundations may be transferred and the salary of their fellowships ingrafted in the new physicians' college and there constitute the fellows of that society. And that none should be transferred till they have been 2 years standing in their original college, nor continue longer in the physicians' college than 3 years after their doctor's degree. But, when they leave it, they may be obliged to communicate all the rare cases in practice or experiments of our own country medicines to the college. It would be necessary that some eminent apothecary and chirurgeon be admitted into the same college to teach the young students those practical arts first. Afterwards let the young student go through a course of anatomy, botany and chymistry and, at last, attend the professors to direct his study and to see their practice upon the poorer sort. The professors of physic, anatomy, chymistry and botany ought to be members of the same foundation and may be chose[n] once in 3 years by the fellows.

This scheme would improve the faculty by the joint endeavours of many ingenious men and, from this college, expert physicians would be sent into all parts of this kingdom.

'Tis certainly a great defect in the education of physicians in the universities that none of their professors teach the practical part but only treat their auditors with notions about which all disputes are unnecessary. And, if those who are to take any degree were obliged to read upon any diseases, as we find by Wedelius (Fig. 35)[109] they do in foreign universities, that exercise would be most useful.

Fig. 35. *Georg Wolfgang Wedel, engraved portrait from Floyer's copy of* Physiologia Medica *(1680), the Library, The Queen's College, Oxford.*

The great expense in degrees and the bachelor's degree ought to be dismissed; the doctor's degree at 7 years standing is sufficient.

If it were possible to erect a hospital in Oxford for the care of the poor, there all the young students would see the practice of physic. And I would advise them to observe first the effects of all the dispensatory medicines and then those of the hospital medicines already published and, after these, to try Bate's and Fuller's prescripts, and to observe all the curious chirurgical operations and those in midwifery. The want of such experiments is the occasion of a young physician's want of employment for some years because in the university he can learn little of the practical part. If the several colleges and the town would join their purses, they might soon erect a hospital for the cure of the poor and the instruction of young students.

I must not forget the great advantage the students might have by the erecting of hot and cold baths. By the hot all the secretions are promoted and by the cold all violent evacuations may be stopped. By the use of the *balnea aqua dulcis*, gangrenes, cancers, consumptions, scurvies and pains, may be prevented; and this would very much preserve the old men who live sedentary lives.

Chapter 4

Concerning the Physician's Charity, Compassion on the Sick and his Fees

'TIS THE DUTY of a physician as well as his interest, to visit the poor when sick, who can give no fees but must be cured gratis. And by this method he will improve his experience and oblige the richer sort to observe his charity and skill. And they will esteem his practice as serviceable to his country and that he is a person of great humanity.

The next act of charity to the poorer sort is to prescribe few or the cheapest medicines and to make some useful ones to give away to them.

'Tis a great act of charity to souls as well as bodies of our patients to give good advice against all intemperence when that occasions a disease; and against inordinate affections which destroy the natural constitution of our humours. He ought to comfort the fearful [and] melancholic and [to] appease the fury of all passions, by proper reasoning and friendly advice; and by showing a sincere concern for the pains of the sick, by a grave and serious discourse and carriage. It will often startle the greatest debauchees when the physician demonstrates to them that a further pursuit of their sensual pleasures will bring a fatal decay on their bodies; and thus the physician may save the soul as well as the body of his patient.

We ought to speak well of our patients and neighbouring physicians and that will oblige both when they hear of it. Though both be very vicious yet 'tis our duty to conceal their faults as well as their infirmities, which we discover by our conversation with them. He that is censorious will certainly be opposed and suffer in his practice by the persons whom he abuses. By the disagreement in consultation the faculty suffers some scandal, and the patient is disturbed and dismisses the turbulent imperious doctor.

By the laws [i.e, custom] of our land fees are due to a physician to repay the great charge of his education; and his attendance gives him as much right to them as any other art or profession does. And in Ecclesiasticus (Ch. 38 V. 2) 'tis said: *he shall receive a gift of the king*. Pliny mentions the great fees given by the Romans:[110] Erasistratus had 100 talents;[111] and the Grecians also gave large fee; and Galen had for curing

59

Boethius's wife,[112] 400 aureos. Hippocrates's method was to agree for a cure, as our chirurgeons do.

Where the fees are moderate the practice is greater, as in Holland and France. And ignorant practisers taking less fees rob the practice from the true physician. The common people will go to the cheapest, and there is no better way to win the ignorant pretenders to physic than by appointing the common people a certain time and place where advice will be given to them gratis. And the prescribing our country simples to be powdered and infused is the cheapest method. And if physicians were bred chirurgeons, as Hippocrates and Galen were, that would supplant the practising chirurgeons and be the best means of introducing young physicians into practice amongst the poorer sort.

Hippocrates was a great lover of his country and refused the noble offers of Artaxerxes;[113] Galen had great repute at Pergamon, his own country, as well as at Rome. He got reputation by using vulgar medicines and curing by diet, exercise, air and baths. That will oblige the vulgar most for, in prescribing many and costly medicines, the physician respects the apothecary more than the patient.

The vices contrary to charity are the unsatiable desire of fees from the poorer sort or the neglect of the poor for want of them [i.e., the fees]. Hippocrates was a great example of the contempt of money and he advises the same to his disciples; and this virtue he called αφιλαργνρια (freedom from avarice). The physician ought to consider the circumstances of their patients and what fees they can bear and to require no more.

Chapter 5

Concerning the Physician's Prudence in Managing his Practice and in his Discourse and Conversation amongst his Patients and in his Prognostication concerning the Event or Changes of Diseases

I WILL COMPREHEND the physician's discretion necessary in practice under these rules.

1. The physician must patiently hear the whole history of his patient's case, to observe all the symptoms and to reduce them to their primary causes in the solids and [the] fluid; and to explain to the patient, so far as he is capable of it, the causes and nature of his disease and the method he designs to pursue in the cure. But, as to the medicines, they are not to be discovered to the imprudent or timorous.

2. 'Tis convenient to gratify the patient in all things which are not injurious to his disease, such as small beer to some and flesh meats when they can do no harm and are earnestly desired.

3. We ought not to use blisters, cupping, bleeding [or] vomits upon all occasions as some do, but to try the gentler methods of diet, exercise, [or] hot or cold baths by which the old physicians cured all their diseases and prevented them; and when they cannot cure, to try the greater remedies, vomits, strong purges [and] salivations; and, at last, to come to issues, blisters, cuppings, punctures, incisions [and] cauteries.

4. [We ought] to imitate nature in our practice to help it by removing any impediments and to proceed gently in fevers, not violently or rashly; but to promote the crises in diseases by stopping the violent or irritating the slow circulation; and in all obscure cases, to do no harm when we can do no good.

5. Hippocrates (Fig. 36) advises not to give any medicines to procure abortion, nor to give any poisonous medicines, and not to undertake any dangerous operations as cutting for the stone, but to leave them to the lithotomists.[114]

6. Hippocrates advises us to design the healths of our patients into whatsoever family we are called and to use chastly and holily the art of physic; to avoid all voluntary wickedness and venereal pleasures and all manner of intemperance, deceit and irreligious discourses or practice which may injure the family; and we must cautiously avoid any discourses with others about our patients' infirmities, especially those of the females.

Fig. 36. *Hippocrates, from C.J. Sprengell,* The Aphorisms of Hippocrates and the Sentences of Celsus *(1708).*

7. We ought not to prescribe more medicines than are necessary for the disease because that gives a disgust to the patients and injures his pocket; and we may observe that children and old people are incapable of a multitude of medicines.

8. The physician ought not to undertake incurable diseases: cancers, old dropsies, leprosy, the stone in the bladder, [nor] epilepsies after age.

9. The physician must satisfy himself after giving a rational advice, though the patient show his dissatisfaction or ingratitude. Such injuries the physician must expect and bear patiently. He must despise all unreasonable accidents of reproach and sleight, which happen through the perfidious or malicious tongues of other physicians or [when] patients deride us. With proud affront the ignorant scandalise our practice and persons. He that studies is called whimsical, and the common medicines old women's receipts. A young physician is

despised for want of experience and the old is esteemed dull and forgetful. How easily are the sick disgusted and the mean practisers misrepresent the actions of the best physicians. All this happens because the patients cannot judge of the physician's ability and his method. And though the case be incurable the physician is dismissed as an unfortunate man. 'Tis a good providence to the physician if he can meet with good success sometimes, to support his credit and procure by his practice a moderate profit to maintain himself, which will outlast what is got by deceit, flattery or other tricks.

10. We must ascribe all honour to God for all our success and not to our own skill or nature; that according to Hippocrates is learned, sufficient and just and seems to use reason and council. This is because nature is directed by God to produce certain effects and these return in a certain order. Therefore nature is the second cause disposed by God for producing all orderly effects and has laws imposed on it by God. Nature performs the crisis, concocts, secretes, expels, and thereby cures diseases; and all this is performed by the circulation of the blood and humours, which were at first contrived by God. All our skill [is] in the management of the circulation, so as to accelerate the too slow and stop the violent motion by such remedies as have been induced by God with such tastes and qualities as will produce those effects. The circulation be the remote cause of some diseases, yet the cacochymias produced by it must be cured by contrary tastes.

I will next consider the physician's prudence in his conversation and discourse and habit in his opposition to superstitious remedies and in his prognostications. It is fit that a physician should have the knowledge of good behaviour and breeding which is a judicious observation of decencies, and this is got by conversation amongst the better sort. These are the general accomplishments which become all men. A familiarity accompanied with respect is most agreeable to men of sense. The court is the academy of good breeding and amongst the company of women 'tis soonest learnt. It requires much art and wit to restrain our humour and not to disturb company. It will require some time to acquire such polite conversation as to observe, not only the ways and customs of our country, but the genius and disposition of those with whom we converse and how to make our carriage and discourse agreeable to them.

Hippocrates recommends modesty and humility. Modesty recommends the physician amongst virtuous women and humility amongst men of good sense. Imprudence will hinder women from their discourse of their infirmities and pride is hated in all people. But much more in a physician because he is as a servant to his patient.

63

Hippocrates recommends cleanliness of habit, not over envious and rich or affected, but decent and modest which is esteemed as a figure of discretion and understanding. And he further advises [us] to sit decently in our visits, to speak little and with gravity, and to do nothing with disturbance or solicitude, to fear nothing, to neglect nothing, to answer readily all objections, to visit often, to consider with attention and care, and [to] take the right opportunities of cure, [and] to avoid all offensive odours and smells, especially of wine and noise, and to consider the place in which the sick lies, but not to discover anything present or to come to the sick, but to others whose concern it is.

Hippocrates further proceeds in his advice to be subtle in word and deed, to use familiarity and affability towards all, frugal in diet and content with little; patient in expecting the success, able to explain all axioms and observations, using eloquence without affectation. By these means the physician will acquire glory, and this is the υπεροχη θεια (God-like authority) recommended by Hippocrates.

Fearfulness is a sign of want of experience, confidence of ignorance. We ought to aim at doing great cures, then to acquire great reputation. The confident and talkative are frequently mistaken.

The physician's humanity towards the sick is the cause of his love of the art and he will magnify it for his cure. Hippocrates advises [us] to assist the stranger and poor before all others; but to be too forward to undertake a cure is despicable, though it be a sign of benignity.

The altering methods when well designed are the occasion of ill success, for nothing can succeed unless medicines are given in due quantity.

Neither the sick [n]or well like austerity and generally avoid such physicians. The physician must not discourse with the vulgar but upon necessary subjects, for they despise those who are familiar with them. And we ought to express ourselves in as few words as we can for *medicus garrulus aegrotanti alter morbus* (a garrulous doctor is another illness to one who is sick). We must avoid all common topics of discourse, as plays, horse races, fashions, meats, wines, entertainments, censuring the conduct of others, or lavish commendations, or invidious comparison or calumniating other practisers.

Too much pleasantness and laughter are troublesome, but the countenance must be composed, not proud or frowning. The γτωμολογια (speaking of wise sentences), is commended by Hippocrates. The physician must be ready to serve, constant in his opinion [and] resolved what to do, as soon as he is fully informed. And first observes the pulse which shows the circulation and secretions; the tongue shows the quality of the lympha lactea of all the conglobate glands; the urine shows the cacochymias in the blood; the colour of the skin is from the same; the heat and cold attend hot or cold cacochymias; the motion, speech [or position in which one is] lying differs according to the heat or coolness and strength or weakness of spirits.

In short, we must consider what character a physician ought to have, and to use the methods which conduce thereto, and observe them nicely: to be moderate to all, grave in company, eloquent and agreeable or, at least, humane.

The subject of the physician's discourse ought to be useful, what may advance the law of virtue and its practice, or reform the exorbitant passions, instruct the understanding, or give advice in difficulties, comfort in affliction, and give a reverent sense of God and honourable opinion of his providence.

By all this prudent conduct we bring wisdom into physic and make that a part of wisdom. It belongs to the prudence as well as to the religion of the physician, to attain that virtue Hippocrates calls αδεια δαιμοτια (inspired fearlessness), and thereby avoid all superstitious tricks in practice. Hippocrates advises [us] not to impute all epilepsies to the Gods but to second causes, for the heathen priests pretended to the cure of them by sacrifices, purifications and charms. The devil then pretended to the cure of diseases as well as inflicting them, and this he did by magical superstitions and dreams in Aesculapius's temples; and by these means promoted idolatry and did many cures in men's bodies, that he might destroy their souls.

We must not now trust to sacrifices, holy water or holy wells dedicated to particular saints; nor to prayers to any saint of particular places or diseases nor pilgrimages to them. The font water was formerly abused after its consecration and therefore was forbid to be used. Many medicines were given in holy water and the consecrated water given to cure. And the words of scripture [were] used in charms and the images of saints laid in springs to infuse virtue into them. Thus the vulgar have been abused by the Roman priests and this was in imitation of the heathen superstition who called their medicines by the names of their heroes, as they do now by that of the saints. And the springs that were dedicated to Diana[115] are now dedicated to the Virgin Mary.

Medicines were to be got at certain times of the moon or under such aspects of the planets and now there are particular days for getting of them. Charms and words were used by Christian priests as well as by the heathen. These had them at first from evil spirits, who suggested them to the Magi who were astrologers as well as physicians. And they persuaded the people that the virtue of medicines as well as diseases depended on the planets and, by that trick, the astrologers became the only physicians.

The Pythagoreans introduced the superstition of numbers, and he was a physician.

We owe some superstitions to the chymists who cure wounds by applying medicines to the weapon; all amulets, stones of serpents, blood stones [and] gems are magnified by them, so as to preserve from thunder and evil spirits.[116] By such superstitious applications of medicines, Satan has deluded men and diverted them to unprofitable methods of cure by which they neglect the use of natural means appointed by God for their cures.

The words of scripture were designed for our instruction and not for the cure of diseases, as they are now used in charms. The insignificant words in charms can have no natural effects nor divine institution. Words have their significance from the institution of men and verses can do no more than words, though Theophrastus[117] says the sciatica may be cured by them, and Cato[118] says verses would help dislocated limbs, and in Homer, Ulysses's haemorrhage from his thigh was cured by a verse; and Sammonicus writ in a paper abracadabra and hung it about the neck to cure agues.[119] Such superstitious practises are heathenish cures and the poets gave credit to them.

Carmuna vel possunt caelo deducere lunam
Carminibus circe socios mutavit Ulixi;
Frigidus in prato contando rumpitur anguis.

Magic spells can inveigle the moon from the sky;
With her magic did Circe transform into beasts
The men of Ulysses; and magic can blast
A cold-clammy snake, as it slides through the meads.

(Translation: C. Day Lewis)

The superstitions yet remaining in physic are: the odd numbers prescribed in physical doses; the small quantity of specific medicines to produce great alterations, and their occult qualities; the meaning of blood stones, eagle stones, serpent and toad stones; the chymical amulets of mercury [and] arsenic; spiders [and] toads; the sympathetic powders; and the use of gems in medicines and bezoar stone; [and] the hanging of roots of plants about the neck for convulsions.

All the magical ceremonies are delusions of the devil who persuades men to depend on uncertain remedies by which many lose their lives. Some unnatural means are part of the heathenish idolatry. No good spirit could suggest such means as create a dependence on unnatural causes; and, if charms have ever succeeded, it is by the help of Satan, because they can produce no natural effects. And no glory is attributed to God for such success nor any dependence on God's blessing can be thought of, for the charms are most used by ignorant people who are the common practisers of this magical physic. Our sacraments did perform great miraculous cures, the Apostles cured by the name of Christ, and our Saviour was dishonoured by the Jews when he did miracles by his word and touch. But all these were true miracles, done by a divine power (Fig. 37). In imitation of these, the Devil prescribed charms, and attributed to them miraculous power exceeding that of their natures. Therefore all their effects depend on the operation of those evil spirits who first instituted them. All the ignorant are confident of the effect of their charms and esteem their success as miracles.

I will lastly consider the prudence of the physician in prognosticating the event of his patient's case. If the cure does not proceed rationally nor the patient is obedient to use proper medicines and diet, 'tis not possible to predict certainly. When the case is evidently incurable, 'tis fit to inform the patient of it that he may discern your honest dealing, and you will escape censure. When we discern great danger we must not use any famous medicine nor violent means, lest the ill success be imputed to that. We must discover the danger to a proper person who may put the patient upon settling his affairs. 'Tis the physician's business to encourage his patient to the use of remedies which sometimes succeed miraculously. If the physician forsakes his patient and he afterwards recover it will be a great disgrace to him, as well as when he predicts health and the patient dies.

We show our skill in prediction when, by the present symptoms, we can discover those which are past and not related; and what changes are like to succeed and if, by applying proper remedies, we prevent other diseases which would succeed. The cure

Fig. 37. *Christ Fasteth, is Tempted, and Overcometh, from Laurence Howel,* A Compleat History of the Holy Bible *(1725).*

will seem the greater if we predict much danger and the patient will more readily obey his prescriptions. But if the greatness of the disease will kill, we ought to declare it and then he will not be blamed. But 'tis the physician's fault if he knows not the history of the disease [nor] its cause, nor cures it rationally, nor predicts truly.

The difference of physicians on a consultation makes the vulgar believe the whole art is conjectural. If a person oft relapses after his cure by a good physician 'tis a sign of its being incurable. In young men and where the most generous medicines have not been tried we may entertain some hope. Where the disease is evidently dangerous we may try an experiment. By a good success we gain reputation, and lose nothing by the ill event. Sometimes a rash attempt succeeds: *quos ratio non restituit adjuvat temeritas* (boldness may revive him whom reason does not restore).

There is a certain propriety in some men, intermittent pulses [and] convulsive motions which are natural; and these may deceive the prognosticator. We ought not to undertake the incurable diseases: blindness, deaf and dumb, foolishness, hereditary stone, gout [and] leprosy. And these diseases are commonly fatal: apoplexy, plague, dropsy, wounds of the heart, brain, bladder, diaphragm, stomach, lungs and great arteries.

The physician must not confidently declare that any one medicine will certainly cure because sometimes such a one does fail upon account of complicated diseases or particular constitutions. If a consultation be desired, it would be inhumanity to refuse it and they who do so are commonly unfit for want of learning. And they who are morose, passionate, obstinate or ignorant ought not to be admitted. If it be desired by the doctor, 'tis for securing his own credit against the common scandal, that the patient miscarries through his ignorance or neglect.

If the physician modestly speaks of his cures in the same case it will create a great confidence in him; but much boasting is offensive and produces a distrust. Whatsoever diseases do stop the circulation or cause it to run too fast, must be esteemed dangerous. Sincerity and veracity are greatly valued by patients; boasting is odious in the serious concern of life and death. In fevers the predictions are uncertain and in them we must take time to collect all the good and bad signs, that we may compare them and observe some of the chief judicatory days in fevers.

The physician ought to declare himself doubtful unless the signs of life or death be infallibly certain. He that predicts well will be admired; he that predicts ill will be derided and esteemed mad, or to desire the death of his patient. By the small alterations in the pulse and respiration we know there is little danger. But the disease may prove mortal if the changes from their natural actions be very great and threaten the stop of the circulation, which runs too fast or too slow and thereby kills.

Chapter 6

The Character of an Ill Physician and some Errors in Physic are Censured

IN THE PRECEDING chapter I have drawn the character of a good physician, who pays due reverence to his Creator and governor of the world [and] who vindicates and declares his belief of his being and ascribes all wisdom and success to him. He uses the greatest industry in getting a perfect knowledge of his profession and in his practice and conversation is easy, humble, prudent, charitable and [is] an enemy to all superstition. The contrary to all these will make the character of an ill physician

1. The first fault is to be atheistical. He is an Epicurean in his philosophy and morality amongst the unlearned or at best a pure deist and jests upon the history of revealed religion (Fig. 38).[120] And, by his

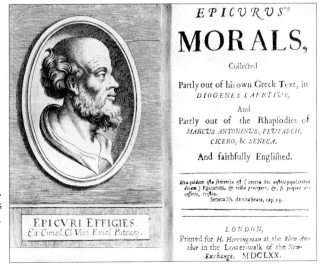

Fig. 38.
Epicurus, Morals
(1670).

69

railery against religion and divines, he procures a reputation amongst all debauchees and he encourages their vicious practices by assuring them of a cure.

2. A bad physician is slothful in his studies and is desperate in his practice for want of time and perfect information and, to vindicate himself, rails against learning and despises all the improvers of the art. He is one of the empirical sect and pretends to experience and nothing more. He says the causes of disease are unknown, as well as the constitutions of men, and the nature of medicines. He oft reads Pliny, Agrippa (Fig. 39)[121] and Montaigne (Fig. 40),[122] to teach him to rail against physic: *nullam artem medicina inconstantiorem* (no art more chancy than medicine). He says a pilot cannot be made by books, though there can be no true artist without the help of reason and a

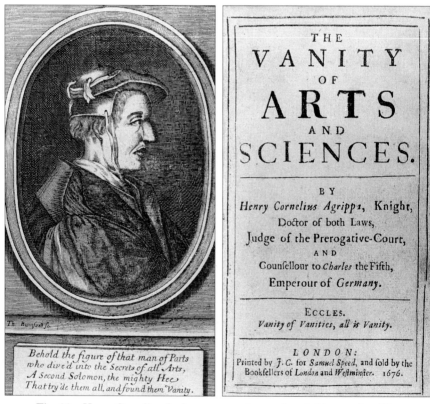

Fig. 39. *Henry Cornelius Agrippa, engraved portrait and title page from* The Vanity of Arts and Sciences *(1676).*

70

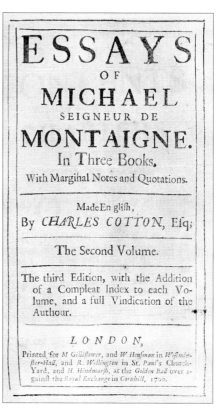

Fig. 40. *Michel de Montaigne,*
engraved portrait and title page from
Essays *(1700).*

long experience which is conveyed to us by the old authors. And, if
we consider an animal body as a machine made of pipes, humours
and spirits, we can easily observe the external causes of our diseases;
how they alter our pulses by stopping or accelerating their motion.
Such are our diet, air and exercises. And anatomy shows us all the
secretions by whose obstruction or evacuation changes happen in the
organicals, which are the seat of the malady. And those are described
in anatomy: the solid parts were made to move and contain, to digest
and secrete the fluids which stimulate or retard the motion of the
solids. And these things we cannot know without the study of anatomy
which represents all these things to our senses. This empirical sect
may justly bear the calumnies of the authors mentioned. *Medicina est*
ars quaedam homicidiorum; experimenta per mortes agunt; evadere fati
ope, non medici (Medicine is a certain art of murderers; its experiments
work through deaths; to escape is by the help of fate, not of doctors).

71

As to ignorant tradesmen who practise to get their bread, they would not persuade their patients to have their clothes, shoes or periwigs made by any person who never served many years to those trades. Yet they impudently pretend to cure though they have not regularly studied that art to qualify them for practice. And, if they chance to cure, we may use the old reflection: *quos ratio non restituit adjuvat temeritas* (what reason cannot restore, audacity may).

3. He is an ill physician who only pursues money or glory. By some indirect means he despises the poor and neglects his cure. He wheedles the women with compliments all day and drinks with their husbands all night. He impertinently brags of his cures and large practice and gives a just occasion to that old saying: *mentire ut medicus* (to lie like a doctor). He talks much of his learning but refuses all consultations of the learned. He conceals his own miscarriages and is always carping at the actions of other physicians. He puts his patients into great fears of death that he may magnify the cures of small infirmities. He prescribes small quantities of medicines at once that he may get more fees; and sometimes changes his method or continues it to an excess. All these are disingenuous tricks to get money from his patients.

4. He is an ill physician who uses any frauds in his practice. When he knows not the cause of a disease he imputes it to poisons, witchcraft and evil spirits and, for the cure, prescribes superstitious characters: image worship, exorcisms, verses for charms, amulets and neglects all natural remedies. 'Tis a usual cheat amongst chymists to pretend to prolong life by gold drops or other arcanas or universal medicines, whereas prolongation of life depends on the right use of the non naturals. The external state of the air in each climate prolongs or shortens the lives of the inhabitants. The Ethiopians grew old about 30 by reason of their great heat. But the Britons formerly lived to 120, the cold preserving their natural heat. This was an observation made by Aesculapius and recorded in Galen. And he makes this useful observation that in most southerly parts they bleed rarely, because the excessive heat promotes perspiration too much; and the cold in the northern parts thickens the humours and over chills them; and the bodies in the most northern are small and ill coloured. But in the intermediate places, the physicians bleed most freely where all evacuations are more moderate. Amongst ourselves we sometimes bleed too much in rheumatisms for want of the use of hot baths and cupping in that disease. An honest doctor will bleed no more than is necessary, for that cannot cure all diseases.

He is a cheating doctor who pretends to a universal medicine made of his minerals. But they are rarely admitted into the blood and because of their gravity cannot mix with the humours, nor be easily expelled out of the body. The chymists will persuade us that all diseases are new and require new medicines. As to prognostications they answer ambiguities as the old oracles did. He is usually a cheat who comes as a stranger and gets half his pay in his hand and removes before his cure be finished. But they deserve to be thus used who value strangers more than their neighbour.

5. He cannot be a good physician who is not of a virtuous conversation. He that is intemperate spends more time in his debauched company than in his study and diligent practice. Any vehement passions of love, envy, anger [or] fear disturbs the physicians mind so much that he cannot discern the whole history of a disease [n]or regularly pursue his method of cure. The old drunkard is stupid, the lascivious goat is odious, [and] the hauty and proud behaviour disgusts. The actions of the passionate are precipitate and are usually avoided. The impertinent and imprudent discourses are disagreeable to wise patients. All profaneness and bantering jests are disrellished by those who think themselves in danger. To deny a visit in time of extremity [or] to answer a languishing patient roughly or scornfully is great inhumanity.

6. He cannot be a good physician who employs all his time in philosophy, geometry, anatomy, chymistry [and] botany: these are the introductory or ornamental parts. But a practice in the art is most necessary; by that we understand the virtues of the medicines and the proper methods of the cure, the diagnostics and the prognostic signs, and the complications of diseases and their successions to one another. The young physician is despised for want of experience and an old one without it is ridiculous; and the vulgar prefer the empiric to the learned doctor. But amongst men of sense, the well read with long experience have the most esteem. He is like the most curious clock maker who knows exactly all the contrivances of his machine, and he has had experience how to regulate the disorderly motions and to restore the decay of his engine. So physicians regulate the exceeding or deficient pulse and correct the effects of them, the cacochymias.

7. He is an ill physician who has [no] time to study to improve his faculty by discovering the virtues of our native simples or finding a more pleasant, shorter and safer method of curing diseases of which he has many experiments; who neglects the writing the history of such or any rare experiments, or to record the histories of the dissections of diseased bodies; nor keeps an account of some experiments made by others in trying the effectual virtues of simple medicines. By these means a physician may show his love to mankind and this will give him an honourable name in his profession after envy for some time has traduced his observations. For the slothful physician censures the labours of others and asperses all new experiments, and they pretend

73

all was anciently known. 'Tis true our present age can only add to old discoveries some useful observations and correct their mistaken notions. But we may observe the same symptoms in diseases and the same method of cure as was formerly in the old writings.

There can be no greater satisfaction to a wise physician than that he has done much good to many in his profession during his life and has discovered something useful for the service of all mankind after his death.

The disgrace of physic[123] in this age depends on these causes:

1. The physicians in the university are better skilled in notions than experience which would give them a right method of cure and the common forms of medicine.

2. The vulgar cannot distinguish betwixt the learned and the experienced doctor and other pretenders. These promise miraculous cures by an infallible medicine.

3. The separation of chirurgery from physic. The vulgar are more sensible of the cures on the external parts, but all inward cures are like charms to them. All physicians were anciently chirurgeons and that helped their reputation amongst the vulgar.

4. The great decay of the present state of physic is owing to the apothecary's excessive bills, which occasions many patients to advise with quacks who sell their medicines cheap. And those who sell their medicines do frequently abuse the patient by excessive rates. The patient may remedy this evil by choosing an honest apothecary; the rich ones cure generally most reasonably. And if simples were introduced they would be less chargeable to both the apothecary and the patient. But this in time will reduce the apothecary to the grade of a druggist[124] and then the physician will ruin the apothecary, as they have now supplanted the physician's practice. These abuses may be corrected by the apothecaries themselves or by some future law to restrain the number of their apprentices, as is done in foreign parts, and by appraising their medicines every year. And the Company of the Apothecaries ought to extend to all the cities of the Kingdom to restrain all abuses, which are the same everywhere. And the ill constitution and education of a physician in England wants some new laws to amend both; and to extend the power of the College of Physicians through the whole Kingdom, and to restore to all graduates in the Universities the privilege of being members of the College.

5. The licenses of all [the] apothecaries [and] chirurgeons by the spiritual courts is a great abuse on the faculty, and makes more practicers than can live by one another.[125] The pay for a licence is under 40 shillings and if they for the future were to pay 50 pounds to the King

that would reform this abuse. These practicers now certify for others, contrary to the design of the statutes. But few of that court would be willing to trust their lives with the advice of those they licence.

6. The old physicians prescribed exercises, and bathing, friction, unction [and] cauterising, but the moderns now use chiefly alteratives which frequently cannot cure without the old practices. The intemperance of this age produces many crudities, scurvies and dropsies, which were formerly cured by abstinence [and] warm baths. 'Tis impossible to eat and drink the exact quantity our constitution requires. Therefore, fasting once a week from flesh meats and strong drinks will prevent many diseases, inflammations, pain, defluxions, fevers, apoplexies, rheumatisms, haemorrhages [and] obstructions, which are the usual effects of a hot and high diet.[126] This fast will teach us to deny our appetites and give the pleasure of a tranquility in our minds, which will be freed from the heat and fury it feels by too hot a diet, and the stupor and oppression which is produced by too much plenty and fullness. Diet was only designed for our supply of the nutriment lost and 'tis pity to destroy so curious a machine by diet, which was designed by providence for support against its decay.

7. Some physicians occasion the disesteem of their art by their spiteful and satirical wit. Other tempers are morose, austere, impatient, [and] insolent and do not prudently connive at the unkindness or ingratitude of their patients. To talk of our patients' diseases or to reveal the secrets of families very much disobliges. We must cure the venereal diseases in women and all hereditary diseases under the names of other diseases, for to speak the whole truth in such cases begets quarrels and disgusts the patient. It is happy for [a] physician to come [as] a stranger into any place and 'tis his interest to be of no party in elections and religious dispute, [n]or those in the State. He must avoid all vulgar recreations and studies foreign to his profession. If a physician has [a] great skill in any part of his profession that will approve respect amongst wise men. This is the duty of a physician to frame some project of curing more speedily, and safely and pleasantly; and for that end, to make some uncommon medicines and to keep them as arcanas if extraordinarily effectual; but, at last, to communicate all improvements in the method of cure or [of] medicines for the benefit of posterity and the honour of his art and country. Since true indications without effectual medicines can cure no disease, we must look for the best specific in every disease: in inflammations and dysentery, when in pains and fluxes, laudanum; in fevers, the cortex; in the lues, mercury; in hysterics, *sal jovis*; in obstructions, steels and bitters and antihecticum; in haemorrhage, alum; in pulmonic diseases, gum ammoniacum and gum guaiacum; in the stone, soap, turpentine, oil [and] salts, and the best sudoric spirit of sal ammoniac; in hot scurvy,

the juice of cool herbs and milk; in saltness of blood, chalybeate or other waters. If we can find the right quantity and method of giving each of these specifics we shall seldom fail to cure. Weak medicines and small quantities make the best physicians despicable. We must practice with the common forms at first and, in time, reform them by rejecting the multitude of medicines and insisting on one taste for the basis of medicines, to which some few may be added upon the account of symptoms.

The virtues of medicines are best discovered by their tastes and by frequent experiments made of them on our bodies. Chymistry only separates the principles but cannot discover the qualities produced by their mixture. We never can discover the texture, figure or proportion of the particles of our medicines; the sensible quality is all we know and all that is necessary. The fire destroys all mucilages and the chymist medicines want that taste. We cure diseases by contrary tastes: the watery, acid, styptic and mucilagenous tastes correct the bitter, salt and acrid humours, by cooling and diluting them; and the acrid, bitter, salt [and] sweet correct mucilagenous humours by fermenting, inciding and attenuating of them.

Plants which have mixed tastes have mixed principles: wormwoods, as bitter styptics, have an oil and essential salt but, as acrids and aromatics, they have volatile oils and salts. If chymists had tasted the general modes of tastes in plants, they would not have omitted the salt pungency in many plants. Nauseousness cannot be discovered by the chymical principle: gentian has the oil and essential, as is in all bitters; and chymistry has not discovered the acrimony in purges. An acrimony, joined with a nauseous taste makes a purger, as in *Cucumis agrestis* [wild cucumber]; and there is much water, and oil and an acrid salt distilled from it.

No empiric can use a specific because it requires these cautions when 'tis properly used:

1. We must make sufficient evacuations before we use it, otherwise it will make a disturbance if there be a fullness of humours; and the evacuation must be suited to the constitution and morbific cacochymia.

2. In practice we must distinguish those several causes of diseases by which they are divided into several species. Besides, many diseases are complicated and some are only symptoms of some other, and a variety is occasioned by some particular constitution. And 'tis necessary to know the ill state and quality of humours, against which we must prescribe contrary tastes; and in a great disease a greater dose and quantity of specific must be used and, a lesser, in small indispositions.

76

3. We must distinguish all our specifics by their tastes which differ much from one another; and we must choose such as is most suitable to each constitution, the cause of the disease and its symptoms; and we must consider nature's crisis that it may not be disturbed, as in gouts. For want of these cautions, old medicines are discredited and new ones invented by chymists.

4. Some moderns revive old exploded notions, as the attraction of medicines.[127] This was as old as Aristotle: *physicor capio ferrum ad magnetum movetur; sic nutrimentum ad membrum, sic helleborus melancholiam, agaricum pituitam, et rhubarbarum bilem trahunt.* (As a philosopher I hold that as iron is moved towards a magnet, so nourishment is drawn towards a limb, hellebore to melancholy, agaric to phlegm and rhubarb to bile). Because they have a similitude in taste but this is notoriously false: hellebore is very acrid, melancholy acrid, agaric bitter acrid, but pituita is slimy sulfoacid, rhubarb has a stypticity which is not in choler, but an oily mucilage. These purgatives are of a contrary nature to the humours. They therefore not only evacuate humours but correct them by contrary tastes and therefore cannot attract them by any similitude of taste or substance. Vegetables cannot attract animals which differ so much in quality and substance.

They who will demonstrate all the nature of pulses must take out the arteries of a man and fix them on a board by glue, or tie them by strings to it; and pump into the artery cut off close to the heart, by a hand-engine.[128] Let the arteries of the arms have their length to the hand, and those to the head their length to the head, and those to the several viscera their length to them, and the aorta down to the knees, and all the small arteries be cut about an inch long. This will show the different celerity of the circulation in several parts and the alteration in general circulation, by pressing and stopping the circulation in any artery.

An ingenious mechanic would make all the arteries in lead, tin or leather, according to the scheme in our anatomic books; and also contrive veins to the choice arteries for the return of water into [the] pump vessel, or of milk if that be used instead of water. I once made a tube of leather for the aorta and pricked holes for each artery and was much pleased in viewing the several spouts.

Chapter 7

Concerning the Evidence which a Physician has from the Fabric and the Actions of a Human Body that there is a God and that there is in the Body a Substance distinct from it (Fig. 41)

HE WHO ONLY views the external figure, beauty and operations of the several members of our bodies, cannot but acknowledge the great wisdom and art used by the great Creator in the framing of such a corporeal machine. But they will much more admire the divine artifice who have

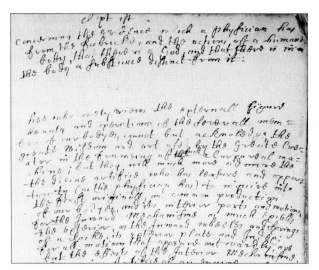

Fig. 41. *Beginning of Floyer's "Concerning the Evidence which a Physician has from the Fabric and the Actions of the Human Body that there is a God" in his* Advice *manuscript, the Library, The Queen's College, Oxford.*

leisure and opportunity (as the physician has) to enquire into the first original and common production of our bodies and its interior parts and motions. For all motions that appear outwardly are but the effects of the internal mechanism. The inward mechanism as much excells the exterior, as the inward wheels and springs of a clock its exterior plate and index. The curious artifice of an engine appears best by seeing its several parts put together at first. So we may observe that several parts of an animal body are daily and successively produced by the incubation of an hen in her eggs, till the foetus arrives at its perfection.

We have no rational account of the origin of mankind but from Moses' history of the Creation, and none but a wise and powerful Creator could form man out of the dust of the earth (Fig. 42). It was impossible that earthy particles, which have no motions of themselves, could put themselves into such mechanical figures and structure. In animals we observe many cavities such as the skull, breast and belly, filled with curious viscera made of the texture of several vessels: the arteries, nerves, veins, lymphatics, glands and their secretory vessels, all which are designed for the containing of different fluids and for the motions of them.

Let us suppose all the mechanical textures of the solid parts and that they be filled in several parts with the humours; yet the body would remain a stupid dead engine till the powerful and wise Creator had breathed into it the breath of life.

Fig. 42. *Man is Created in the Image of God, from Laurence Howel,* A Compleat History of the Holy Bible *(1725).*

That is till, by an impulse of the external air, the circulation of humours was begun. The first inspiration compressing the blood in the vena cava forced it into the right auricle and that projected it into the right ventricle, which further projected it into the lungs to stimulate them into a new inspiration. The return of the blood into the left ventricle is promoted by the contraction of the lungs in expiration and by the subsiding of the breath. The left ventricle, like a pump, projects the blood through the arteries, and the inspiration makes a return of the blood from the veins of the breast. The descent of the diaphragm compresses the cavity of the belly and forces up the blood in the veins of the belly by every inspiration; and the return of the blood from the limbs depends on the force of the

Fig. 43. *Sir Charles Holt, a friend of Floyer and fellow microscopist, Aston Hall, Birmingham.*

heart and arteries and the restitution of the solid parts to their natural tension. When they are distended by the impulse of the heart and the valves support the weight of the blood in its ascent to the heart, the pulse and respiration do naturally assist each other in promoting the circulation in which the life of an animal consists.

In Adam the circulation began from the first inspiration as I have described it. In the womb the foetus lives by the circulation and respiration of its mother but, as soon as it first breathes the circulation alters its course through the lungs and then its inspiration promotes the return of blood instead of [by] the umbilical vein inserted into the vena cava.

Since the earth was a solid dense substance unfit for the formation as well [as the] nutriment of an animal body, it required some fusion or colliquation by a powerful hand. The ordinary matter from which our bodies are now produced is a fluid chyle or serum. A fusion seems intimated by the text χουζ derived from χεω. 'Tis certain air and water are intermixed with all our humours, and the solid parts contain most of the earthy element. As trees and plants were not produced at first from their seed but in a perfect state with their fruits and seeds and able to attract their nutriment, so it was necessary that man should be produced in a mature age that he might help himself and choose his food and receive the commands of his maker, which Moses has described in his history of the Creation.

So great is the mystery of our present generation, as the most curious anatomists confess, all seems as miraculous as the first production of a human body. For the naked eye can discover little of the embryo but that it is lodged in the cicatricula of an egg, as appears by the growth of the chicken betwixt the white and yolk where a *punctum saliens* is observed after incubation.[129] Malpighius[130] by his microscope observed: *pulli stamina in ovo praeexistere altioremque originem nacta esse fateri convenit.* (It is [therefore] proper to acknowledge that the first filaments of the chick pre-exist in the egg and have a deeper origin exactly as [the embryo] in the eggs of plants, Fig. 45). His glasses discovered some larger lineaments of the embryo which are nervous, but how these can be produced from the solid and fluid parts of the parents' bodies is not yet understood. Our learned Harvey[131] gives this remark on generation: *latent veluti in alta nocte prima natura stamina, et subtilitate sua non minus indenia, quam oculorumaciem eludunt.* (The first threads of nature's weaving commonly lie hidden in the depths of night and by their subtlety elude the keenness of the intellect no less than of the sight). Malpighius only directs us to observe the successive manifestation of the parts of animals. And he first observes the appearance of the head and spine and then the heart, arteries, veins [and] umbilical vessels; after them the viscera, liver, spleen, kidneys, stomach [and] guts. That all these solid parts should be pure membranes at first folded up in a little speck or macula; and that the eggs should be filled with proper juices to nourish those solids and to extend them; and that all the successive changes should be made by the

Fig. 44. *Illustrated title page from Floyer's copy of Antonie van Leeuwenhoek,* Epistolae *(1687), the Library, The Queen's College, Oxford.*

heat of the hen in 3 weeks time is, above all terrestrial phenomena, most wonderful and evidently demonstrates the wisdom and power of the Creator in making such curious machines, and giving one machine power to produce another of the same kind. But if we suppose an animalculum injected by the male into the female, how can we accommodate Malpighius's observations and these discoveries of animalcula swimming in the semen? These are very active but that in the macula without motion; how was it possible for an animal to be projected into the ovarium? Who can inform how or where that was formed in the male? Has that any seed for its production? If not then our present philosophers are mistaken who affirm that no animal is produced without a seed. And this animalculum is equivocally produced and only fed in the seminal liquor of the male. This must certainly at first be produced from the

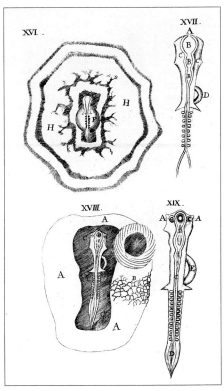

Fig. 45. *Embryonic Observations of Egg Incubation, from Marcello Malpighi,* Anatomie Plantarum *(1675-79).*

membranous parts and juices in the male, as the seeds are in plants and some worms in animals. Since the pre-existing parts which are solid are membranes they are produced from the membranes of the male and all membranes consist of a texture of nervous hollow fibrillae. They will contain some of the lympha and spirits of the male without which it could have no motion. The various configurations of these membranes produce the arteries and veins and glands which Malpighius calls *sacculi membranosi*. The muscles have their original from the arteries since their fibres receive the blood that circulates through them. The nerves arise from the cortical glands and they [the cortical glands] from the arteries. The nerves are the chief instruments of all animal actions. The lymphatics receive their serum from the arteries and all these vessels and their proper juices are originally in the animalculum. No art but the divine wisdom could produce or fold up so many kinds of vessels and their juices in so little a body as the animalculum has. 'Tis at first invisible, though at last it produces a large animal.

I will next consider the different actions of the solid parts and that the anatomist cannot discover the immediate cause of animal motions and how they are produced. There are many natural and perpetual motions in an animal body and others which are voluntary. The natural [and] perpetual motions are the pulsation of the heart, the respiration, the peristaltic motion of the gut, and the secretion of humours. The voluntary motions are done by the motion of the several muscles when we please.

We know that the spirits come into the muscles by the nerves inserted into their fibres and, if the nerves be tied with a thread, that the muscles cannot move. We see [that] the blood gives a deep tincture to the muscular fibres and if the artery which carries it be tied that will hinder all muscular motion. But who can explain the action of the animal spirits on the blood in the fibres by which they are contracted, [or] the fancy of the animal spirits acting on the globuli by their acrid points? The supposition of attraction in the spirits or the explosion of the spirits are modern imaginations or philosophic dreams, which cannot be proved but are supposed by the mathematician doctors; and they can never explain the quick changes of our motions nor what can stop [them] at pleasure.

These natural motions help or stimulate one another. The circulation to the brain propels the spirits into the muscles of the heart and helps its contraction by which new spirits and a new stimulus are sent to the brain; and there the animal spirits are secreted through the cortical glands and the blood is returned from the head by the pulsation of the membranes, which have a diastole and systole at the same time as the heart beats; and this sends the blood down the jugulars. And this is the *first circulation* which, for distinction's sake, I call the *cephalic* (Fig. 46).

In every 5 pulses there is one respiration. The blood projected from the right auricle stimulates an inspiration and the expiration forces the blood into the left ventricle; and that which passes into the muscles of the thorax returns into the cava by motion of the muscles which raise and contract the breast; and the circulation in the arms, shoulders and back, which respect the cavity of the breast and diaphragm, and we must reckon as parts of the *second circulation*, which I call *pulmonic*, as the neck and outward parts of the head are parts of the cephalic circulation. The respiratory motion cannot help the return of blood through the head; it was necessary that the veins should have a pulsation and systole and diastole, as there is in the porta, the same to force the return of the blood to the heart. But since the *third circulation* is in the *coeliac artery* to the guts and viscera and glands and omentum; and the blood runs more slowly through this circle because of its many secretions through the glands (of which

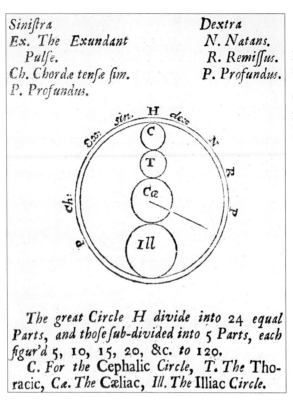

Siniſtra
Ex. The Exundant
    Pulſe.
Ch. Chordæ tenſæ ſim.
P. Profundus.

Dextra
N. Natans.
R. Remiſſus.
P. Profundus.

Fig. 46. *Floyer's imaginative concept of "the Several Circulations and Natural Pulses"*, The Pulse-Watch, Vol. II (1710).

The great Circle H *divide into* 24 *equal Parts, and thoſe ſub-divided into* 5 *Parts, each figur'd* 5, 10, 15, 20, &c. *to* 120.
    C. *For the* Cephalic *Circle,* T. *The* Thoracic, Cæ. *The* Cæliac, *Ill. The* Illiac *Circle.*

nature all the viscera are); it returns by the porta into the cava and that has a pulsation to help the secretion of bile and the blood. The muscles of the belly may belong to this circulation as well as those of the stomach and guts.

The *fourth circulation* is by the *emulgent arteries and the iliac and uterine or seminal vessels*; and the return of this circulation is into the vena cava.

The origin of the artery from the heart [with] the proportionable division of its branches into the several parts [and] the continuation of them with the veins and lymphatics for the management of the circulation of the humours, [and] their forcing the secretion in several parts, is very much to be admired; as well as the curious fabric of the heart, its auricles, valves, ventricles, spiral fibres, its motions, [and] importing and exporting vessels. All these things could never have been, but by the wisest agent who knew all the laws of motion and proportion of tubes necessary for such parts of an engine designed for life and to be a self mover.

The preparation of chyle in the stomach, the conveyance of it through the lacteals, the circulation of it with the blood and their mixture in the lungs, in its arteries and veins, and the secretion of many humours from it and the blood by the glandular viscera, and the return of many of the same into the blood with the new chyle, are most admirable mechanical artifices which none but the most excellent wisdom could contrive. These things will surprise the most atheistical person with wonder and admiration.

With what wonderful art are the organs of our senses framed - the eye, the ear, the taste, smell, and feeling - that, through these, the external objects might produce representations of themselves, and the various colours, smells, tastes, sounds and all the tactile qualities, heat, cold, hard [and] soft? These perceptions of our senses and all the ideas arising thence are made upon the organ filled with animal spirits. But they cannot be explained by any hypothesis in mechanics, because no motion nor figure nor organisation of pipes full of humours can produce any perception, reflection or thought. 'Tis evident that the image of the object appears in the eyes as in a glass, yet that cannot move any membranes. The animal spirit only can receive the impression from the external light, but this cannot cause the vision of the image because the spirits move through many distinct fibrillae in the optic nerves, and those lie in crooked lines, as Malpighius has described them. So that an image cannot be conveyed entire and directly to the brain, but it must be multiplied by the number of the optic fibrillae. Then no distinct vision can be made in any part of the brain, but all vision must be made in the eye itself where our soul sees the figured light on the animal spirits or feels their motion. The fibrillae of all nerves are in the glandules of the brain and there is no place in them for the lodgement of any sensible ideas such as an image. The nerves are nothing but a [fa]sciculus of fibrillae lapt in a common membrane and their cavities are as invisible as the spirits themselves.

'Tis impossible that an impressed image should continue in the spirits when the object is removed, because that is but motion in them and the spirits are a thin fluid. So water, when moved by a stone thrown in, soon loses its undulation. This happens sooner in the air which is a thinner fluid and that by its tenuity, invisibility [and] elasticity, very much resembles the animal spirits. And if the air be moved by voices or bells none of these impressed motions continue long but gradually cease. Fire is the most fluid of all elements and the most elastic. It receives its pyramidal figure from the incumbent air. Its essence consists in a violent motion of rarefied air, which carries the inflamed particles of other bodies with it and this soonest loses all its impressed figures. The light is the most fluid of all fires, being a thin flame and this may be easily reflected and refracted into diverse figures; but these all cease by the interposition of a solid body which reflects the rays of the sun.

Since the spirits have the fluidity of water, the elasticity of air, and the activity of fire and the lucidity of light, we must acknowledge that, though they receive some figure or motion from external objects, yet they must soon lose such impressions by their fluidity. And no ideas can be impressed on the solid parts nor can their pores be altered, for the whole brain consists of glands and excretory vessels, the nervous filaments which contain the spirits diluted by lymph. All motion from the object must terminate in the glands which continually receive new spirits and that would extinguish all impression from the object. And the new object and the motions of passions must deface all former ideas from the senses. These reflections show that we are as ignorant of the method whereby our memory must be explained as we are how sensation is performed. The solid parts of each organ of sense are firmly united to the body and are thereby made incapable of any nice shake by the light, air [or] odour. But in the grosser senses of tasting and of feeling, the external motion may agitate the spirits included in the nervous papillae. Nothing can better represent the external light than the spirits which are naturally luminous. What can better represent sounds than the aerial spirits in animals? What is more like odour than the spirits which are the rarified particles of blood which with the air composes the spirits? But no place in the nerves can so well represent the object as the sensory [organ] itself, which is designed for that use. The nerves serve only to convey the spirits into the organ which is their natural motion. The reflex motion is unnatural because it must ascend through different fibrillae and there is no place in the brain where they unite all the parts of an idea. The impression of an object appears in the organ most vigorous and therefore must there only be perceived, and not in the nerves. Neither is there known any common seat in the brain whither all perceptions are brought and where the sensible soul resides. For all the fibrillae of the nerves arise from different glands. All that matter or animal spirits can do towards the perception of an object is to represent the image or motion to a sensible soul in its organs.

The spirits themselves are a loose congerie of globules which all fluids have. And a multitude of globuli which are incoherent can never be capable of perception, nor capable of making any reflection that they do perceive and know such ideas and that they come from external objects. Can flame, water, air [or] light, by any organisation become sensible or discern their own acts? These fluids cannot lose their natural properties. By being included and moved in their organical vessels they may never thereby acquire sensation. The lympha in which the spirits swim will retard their motion toward the brain. Water is a natural speculum and that will help the representation of objects; and it undulates on the least touch. Tastes and smells are easily imbibed by it. And water will reflect sounds and the air will raise it into tempestuous waves. By the glands of the brain we are certain that there is a pellucid lympha in the nerves such as that in the eye; and the nerves are but secretory vessels to the cortical glands. Since the animal spirits are a mixture of air, water and the volatile particles of the blood which Hippocrates calls fire, we cannot assert that such a compounded body is the sensible soul, [and] conscious of its own acts. But it must be something distinct from all elementary bodies and of an aetherial substance and acts in the body like an angel.

Not only the structure of the solid parts [is] to be admired, but also the production, motion of and colature of the fluids from the blood testify to us a divine artifice. 'Tis a curious piece of chymistry to extract a chylous milk out of all our meats and, out of that liquor, to produce blood and, from that, diverse secretions by the help of the glands of diverse colours, tastes [and] consistence. In our stomach all meats are dissolved by the help of the saliva and then they are fermented by the same; the effects of which fermentation we discern in the contents of the stomach by the foetor of the flesh digested, and a volatile acidity from our vegetable diet and by the swelling and windiness of the stomach after eating. Birds and fish have no diaphragms and therefore cannot help or cause the digestion by the motion of the solid parts.

Some affirm those parts can only shake the stomach and promote or irritate the peristaltic motion and that could never dissolve bones. Therefore digestion is by a fermentation and that changes the nature of vegetables into animal humours. And the flesh we eat putrifies in our stomachs where, by the heat, and ferment from its glands and the air contained in our diet, all these digest, putrify, and turn the dissolved liquor into the nature of each particular animal before that tincture descends into the intestines. And the bile by its bitterness and acrimony corrects the acidities of the stomach and gives it its milky colour and begets the sulfo acid taste in the chyle. The circulation changes the chyle into blood and the serum is produced from its waterish [parts], its nutritious fibres from the caseous parts, and the salt and choler from the oily parts. And out of these principles are all the secretions made through the glands, which is called the *third digestion*. But nature's methods are too fine for our apprehension. 'Tis become the skill of the wisest mechanics to imitate the circulation and the secretion of humours.

This is my usual scheme of animal humours. From the chyle are secreted: (1) the slimy lympha of the stomach and guts, the saliva in the mouth, and the pancreatic lympha; (2) the milk in the breasts; and (3) the seminal liquor, designed for the nutriment of animalcula. All these are compounded of the watery element in the chyle and of its fibrous, its crude oil and false acid particles. In these a mucilagenous oil prevails.

From the buttery part of the chyle [are secreted]: (1) the fat lodged chiefly in the omentum, (2) the red parts of the blood and (3) the choler. [This] is from the oily part of the chyle after a long circulation, and this is mixed with a mucilage [and] an acrid salt. And [it] is very bitter and it gives the colour and bitterness to the urine, sweat and stools.

From the tartar acid in the chyle is produced the vitriolic acid of the blood which may be tasted in all healthful blood, and then is separated in the spleen with a slimy humour from its glands. And this gives the blackness to the spleen and circulates into the porta for the use of the liver.

From the serum of the chyle [is produced]: (1) the serum of the blood, which has an ammoniac saltness and watery and caseous parts; (2) the lymphatics [which] contain a more glutinous lympha or a purer lympha in the eyes and nerves; and (3) the excrementitious salt serum in the sweat and urine. All the serum lymphas have more of . . . fibrous parts, or less, besides the water and saltness. In all secretions there is a serum which is the common vehicle of all of them.

What is necessary to be known is the number, colour, consistence and tastes of the secreted humours and the changes of these by diseases. And all these things are evident in our senses, but the figure of the particles of fluids and their motions will always be arcanas. Salts themselves are compound bodies and consist of different principles, the quantity and manners of whose mixture and motion no person can ever describe. Therefore we must esteem all the over nice mechanical discourses about the pores and secretions to be as tedious and useless as the old atomical cant, for they suppose motions and figures which they cannot see or prove. All their enquiries belong to anatomy and their learned hypotheses are lately demolished by Magalotti (Fig. 47), who asserts they have not sufficient observations on which they can fix their demonstrations about the secretion of humours or their quantity.[132]

I will next proceed to prove that there is in our bodies some substance which we call our spirit or soul which is made of none of our elements, fire, air, water [or] earth. Though Hippocrates calls the soul a mixture of fire and water, the animal spirits are senseless of themselves and are the instruments representing the external objects. But the soul has in itself the faculty of intuition and [of] feeling pain and pleasure. It discerns figured light and undulating air, the resistance of solids and [the] substance of fluids [and] the particles of tastes and the activity of smells. All this it does by the help of the animal spirits and without them the soul can do nothing in the body. The soul is conscious that the impression comes from the object and that it perceives an idea which it can remember, distinguish and argue about. And these acts no matter is capable of performing.

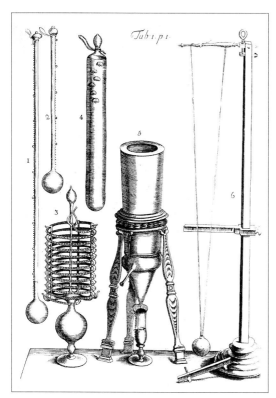

Fig. 47. *Instruments to measure heat and cold, from
Lorenzo Magalotti,* Essayes of Natural
Experiments *(1684).*

Imagination is a representation of the object when it is removed from our senses and the soul can renew all sensible ideas when it pleases. No perception is in any sense when the soul gives no attention to them. But by them, when it pleases, it can discern the whole history of nature, its production [and] changes of motion, alone in the beastly order and preservation of the whole world. And from thence the soul concludes that there was a wise and powerful Creator and, since we perceive how variously the soul acts in its sensation, imagination, judgement and conscientious reflection on our actions, we thence naturally infer that they are the actions of a governing spirit within us. Our knowledge increases by observation of causes and effects. By tradition, by revelation and making inferences from experiments, and by long experience, we make general rules in every science to help the memory and understanding of learners in an art.

The general ideas as well as the reflect, act on them and the work of an intelligent being which considers only the general nature of things in which all particulars agree; and this proves our souls to be of the nature of angels who perceive, judge, reflect, remember and have self motion in themselves. This spirit within us acquires all its arts and sciences by reasoning from sensible observations, but we owe to revelation and to the tradition of it all our religion which our natural reason could not discover. Such is the Creation, incarnation and sacrifices, the last judgement and conflagration of the world.

We feel and experience in ourselves a liberty of thought and actions and that we can determine them to what object we please, but all the motions of the elementary matter are necessarily forced by external causes and it cannot determine or perceive its own motion. It must be something above natural bodies, which is conscious of its own good actions which are conformable to reason and religion and done in order to obtain a new happy state hereafter; and condemns itself when, through incogitancy, perverseness or pleasant sensual allurement, we act contrary to the rules of reason or religion. We cannot observe any matter never so much externated, that has motion in itself or sensation. All motion is given to it by its Creator and all changes of the natural motions must depend on angelical spirits. So the soul is the choice governor of all the motions in the body and mind, except the vital functions such as the pulse and respiration. The divine wisdom would not think it fit to trust the soul with its own life for fear of the ill use of that power.

The soul moves the tongue, voice [and] limbs at its pleasure. It checks the passions by wise reflection, for some pleasing objects occasion a violent motion of spirits to the heart and some members. It is in the power of the soul to stop the actions excited by the passions. But they are more easily prevented by this reflection that all excess in passions destroys the body, though a moderate use of bodily pleasures prospers it. Other objects grate on the body or offend the senses and create a violent aversion, such as pains, diseases, hunger [and] thirst. These impatient emotions the soul restrains by wise reflection. Who can imagine that any sense of pleasure or pain should be governed by a pure machine? Can any such consider before their action and then refuse to act and reflect after action and stop, accelerate and repeat any action, according to its pleasure?

The sensible soul in a man is no way distinguishable from the rational, for that perceives all sensible things; but when it delights only in sensible pleasures we think it brutal. But we call the soul rational as it considers the causes of things, the agreement and disagreement of ideas, [and] the justice of actions, and as it directs them according to divine or human laws in expectation of a better immortal state. These are the actions of a different substance from our bodies, a rational governor and self mover of the bodily actions. But no self motion, no designed and voluntary action, can be performed by any corporeal engine. There is the same difference betwixt the soul and body as betwixt a man and an instrument he uses. Though the soul, by being used to the impressions in the body from its humours and by communicating its motion to all the members, does esteem the body as part of itself till it makes use of its reason and revelation.

The soul knows nothing of its own original, whether God made it with the angels or whether one soul can beget another; these things are not revealed. We know the soul within us by its actions, as we know there is a God by His Creation and miraculous actions above the power of nature. But we know that ourselves in the next world will be like angels both in our state and actions. And now our souls have the same aetherial substance, the same faculties of understanding and sensation, the same liberty of will and actions, as the angels have, though in a lower degree. Because the soul is enclosed in a human body and obliged to govern it by the rules of virtue and religion, the angels now govern all human affairs both public and private, and the same will be the employment of human souls. They will be made ministering spirits in the next state and have glorious incorruptible bodies like the angels.

The great similitude betwixt souls and angels gave rise to the old opinion that all souls descended from Heaven and that to die was to return into their own country whence they came. The Jews had such opinion of the preexistence, when they asked our Saviour whether man sinned or his parents because he was born blind. And in the Wisdom of Solomon, it is said: *Yea, rather being good, I came into a body undefiled* (Ch 8, v 20); and in Ecclesiastes: *Then shall the dust return to the earth as it was: and the spirit unto God who gave it* (Ch 12, v 7). And if the history of our Saviour be considered, he had a body prepared for his soul before it descended from Heaven, and that instance makes this conjecture more aggreeable.

I think 'tis the physician's duty to make these reflections upon brutes, upon whom he exercises a severe dominion.

1. They have the same organs for sensation as men have, the same parts of the brain, a glandulous cortex and fibrillae in the nerves, and consequently the same animal spirits. The external objects impress the same ideas of colour, sounds, tastes [and] smells; and some brutes exceed the faculties of men in their nice sensations. And since they have the same ideas, they have the same imagination and memory, and some more imperfect judgement in acquiring their food and in providing for their foetus. These mental actions are strong arguments that there is a being in them who is a self mover and governs their actions. Their life consists in the circulation of their blood; and some of them have arts, as the spider weaves, and the bee builds its combs, and the birds nest.

2. We may conjecture that the souls in brutes were in some former state before our Creation and now they are evil angels embodied and condemned to lead a painful and miserable life under the dominion of men. They have some inward reasoning though they cannot express it, but in those two instances which the scripture gives which mentions the deceitful arguing of the serpent with Eve and Balaam's ass (Fig. 48) who reproved his master; then the ass's tongue was loosed from its natural impediment.[133] And some birds do imitate the voices of men. And for want of speech brutes cannot improve their reason.

Fig. 48. *Balaam's Ass Speaketh, from Laurence Howel*, A Compleat History of the Holy Bible *(1725)*.

NUMBERS CHAP. XXII.
Balaam's afs fpeaketh.

NUMBERS 22.Verfe 28.

And ÿ Lord opened ÿ mouth of ÿ afs, and fhe faid unto Balaam, what have I done unto thee, that thou haft fmitten me thefe three times?

242.

3. The brutes here are in a miserable state of punishment. They suffer hunger, pain, diseases [and] hard labour, from the cruel usage of men or for getting their food. They use many tricks for getting their prey. Every creature has its enemy to destroy it and keeping its species from increasing too much. They see their young devoured before their eyes and, betwixt men and other animals, they live in continual fear of death. The only pleasures they enjoy are in their food and generation. [And] these are not equal to their sufferings by the injuries of seasons, the scarcity of provisions, sometimes the cruelty of beasts of prey, and the butchery of the most carniverous master, man. For these reasons we conjecture that their lives are a state of condemnation and punishment of some wicked spirits; or else these things are unintelligible to us. And wheresoever men sinned the brutes were swept away by war [and] famine. The murrain and the flood reduced them to their original numbers.

The scripture seems to favour this opinion that evil spirits were embodied in brutes, since Eve was tempted by the serpent who persuaded her that she would not die by eating the forbidden fruit but that it was pleasant and would make her wise (Fig. 49). From then he was cursed above all cattle, though he was esteemed most subtle of all of them and there began the enmity betwixt the seed of the woman and that of the serpent. Then the serpent was accounted as one of the cattle and beasts of the field. And that this serpent that spoke was the deceiver, Satan, and father of lies. And dust he should eat all days of his life that in daring his being there embodied in the serpent, but he had a seed of serpents of the same nature for his posterity, more evil angels so embodied; and the woman's seed was all mankind, which have a natural abhorrence of serpents and their poisonous bites. For this reason the devil had entry to mankind because he was subject to

Fig. 49. *The Fall of Adam and Eve, from Laurence Howel,* A Compleat History of the Holy Bible *(1725).*

93

the dominion of men, and his empire in time was to be destroyed by the son of God born of the woman. But, in the meantime, when the devil was delivered from the serpent, he seduced man to idolatry and brought him to the absurdity of worshiping many brute creatures and the serpent. He had altars, sacrifices and temples for the worship of himself and his priests [and] oracles. And these were the corruptions of the worship of the Creator delivered to Adam and his posterity. If we do not admit the embodying of evil spirits in brutes we cannot understand the history of Eve's temptation, nor the 20th chapter in the Revelation wherein the dragon is bound by the angel: *that old serpent, which is the devil and satan.* That the evil spirits are capable of going into brutal or human bodies is evident by their possessing of man and of the swine in our Saviour's days. And now they can assume the shape of a "soul" or [of] an angel. They now work on the imagination of witches with pleasant visions and dreams. Why should brutes suffer if their souls are not offended and thereby deserved a cruel death and be food or sacrifice for men's sins? To be slain on any account is a punishment, and 'tis commanded, when we eat them, that the blood be poured forth and in sacrifices 'tis to be poured at the foot of the altar.

Not only the dominion of mankind and the image of his maker have occasioned this enmity of the devil, but God's mercy showed to mankind by his redemption after his fall has been the occasion of persecution of all holy men to this day. Hell was a place of torment designed for evil spirits from the foundation of the world and the same will be the punishment of evil men. From here we may infer that the evil angels sinned before the foundation of the world, but men could not sin before a law was given. But men have the same angelical nature because capable of the same punishment; but good men will supply the place of the fallen angels in a future state.

4. We may observe that brutes have no sense of God or religion. Their thoughts are determined to sensual pleasures. They have the same vicious passions as men: revenge, rage, vehement love, [and] fear of death. Their souls are slaves to their bodies and to their natural inclinations and they prey on one another without mercy.

5. We know the creation of brutal bodies, but their souls are unknown to us because we have no revelation about their substance and their first original. And the scripture only tells us that men's and beasts' bodies are made of the earth and all turned to dust again. But as to their spiritual, *Who knoweth the spirit of man that goeth upward, and the spirit of a beast that goeth downward [to the earth]?* (Ecclesiastes Ch 3,v 21). This is the utmost we can learn from Solomon, that they have some different state which none can describe.

6. We find great use from many animals. We were clothed at first with their skins and the northern nations now use the same clothing. Their hair, wool [and] silk yield material for our garments; and the flesh is now since the flood our chiefest nutriment. But their blood is poured forth to this day like a sacrifice. This constitution that was given to Noah and all his posterity, because in that consists the life of an animal and by that an atonement was made at the altar; this like the forbidden fruit is now a trial of our obedience; 'tis recommended by the apostles and was the practice of the Greek church from the beginning, and was observed by the Western churches till transubstantiation was established. The first knowledge of the body was obtained by the priests who sacrificed and by the killing of beasts for diet. But the most severe treatment is the experiments tried on the live brutes, which ought to be seldom practised because we are commanded to be merciful to our beasts. And whether beasts may be restored to enjoy peace [and] plenty of that paradise they lost when sin turned them with Adam out of it, is not improbable, because the happiness of those times [is] described by Isaiah: *The wolf and the lamb shall feed together, and the lion shall eat straw like the bullock; and dust shall be the serpent's meat. They shall not hurt [n]or destroy in all my holy mountain, saith the Lord* (Ecclesiastes Ch 65,v 25).

If we look into the whole history of angels, they appeared like men, they bring messages, sing hymns, they move from place to place; their glorious faces, feet and hands are described. And since we are to be like the angels in our celestial bodies and employments hereafter, we may infer that angels have bodies and [that] they are organised whereby they see the most glorious objects. And they do hear since they are employed in singing hymns of praise and [in] conversing with one another. They have a self motion in themselves and their bodies are described with the same figure as ours but in greater perfection and beauty, theirs of an aethereal and ours of a terrestrial matter. Moses and Elias appeared to the apostles as men and the figure of our Saviour's glorious body is described in Revelation: *His head and his hairs were [white like woo]l, as white as snow; [and] his eyes [were as] a flame of fire; [and] his feet like burnished brass . . . and his voice as the sound of many waters; . . . his countenance was as the sun shining in his strength* (Ch 1,v 14). And when our Saviour was transfigured, his face did shine as the sun and his raiment was white as the light. Our body must rise incorruptible, glorious [and] powerful, and we must bear the image of Christ's heavenly body as we have of the earthly. But this change will be after Christ's millenary reign into which men who are true Christians will arise with the same bodies in which they lived here, and enjoy a happy life in a terrestrial paradise for a thousand years under the reign of our Messiah. We pray for his kingdom: *Thy kingdom come that thy will may be done on earth as it is in Heaven.* By the book of Job (Ch 19,

v. 26), we know the patriarchs believed in a resurrection of the body; and in Hebrews, Abraham looked for a city whose builder and maker is God (Ch 11, v 10). This tradition was soon corrupted by Noah's posterity of a belief into the transmigration of souls, since the whole earth was possessed with this tradition. The old tradition was corrupted by this fable which was conveyed by Noah's posterity into our Western parts, as the old history of the druids testified. Therefore all mankind did concur in this opinion that human souls were capable of different states and changes of their bodies. But the heathens expected it in this world and we in the new Heaven [and] the new earth. If there be any truth in it, the souls of brutes or evil spirits can only transmigrate from one body to another for that opinion cannot consist with a future judgement, for good or ill actions done in the body.

If we consider the effects of a violent conflagration (which has been observed in the burning concave vessels opposed to the sun), all mineral, vegetable and animal substances will melt into glass by the heat of the sun; and minerals mixed with vegetable ashes produce a glass like to precious stones, and such is the building of the new Jerusalem in the new earth (Fig. 50). Her light was like a jasper stone, clear as crystal. The city was pure gold like to clear glass, and the foundation of the walls of the city were adorned with all sorts of precious stones. This experiment demonstrates to us the possibility of the conflagration of this world and that, from this world burnt, will arise a glorious new earth as is described in the scriptures. Our earth was at first made from the chaos of an old world that was afterwards changed by the flood; and the present state will be changed by the conflagration into a new Heaven and [a] new glorious earth. There will be no sea in it, nor aerial atmosphere, nor elements, which must all melt by the fervent heat, except a pure river of water in which there are no terrestrial particles. There will be no need of the sun or stars because the lord God will be a light to His saints. There can be no corruption in that state where there is no air, [n]or sea, [n]or corruptible bodies. The description of an angelical body is given us in Daniel: *A man clothed in linen, whose loins were girded with fine gold [of Uphaz]; his body was [also] like the beryl, [and] his face as the appearance of lightning, and his eye as lamps of fire, and his arms and feet [like] in colour to polished brass, and the voice of his words like the voice of a multitude* (Ch 10, v 5). This was the glory of an angel's body and ours at last shall be like it.

The bodies of wicked men may be reduced by a conflagration into an incorruptible state and so be condemned to eternal burnings. Or else, we are told in scripture, that God can destroy both body and soul in Hell, which is called the second death; and death and Hades will be thrown with all sinners into the burning lake. That is none shall die any more, nor will there be any place for the dead in the world to come after the

REVELATION CHAP. XXI.
The Heavenly Jerusalem.

REVELATION 21. Verse 22.

And I saw no Temple therein, for the LORD GOD *almighty, and the* LAMB, *are the Temple of it.*

Fig. 50. *The Heavenly Jerusalem, from Laurence Howel,* A Compleat History of the Holy Bible *(1725).*

second resurrection. The sun may be the πυρ αιωτ (eternal fire), whose fire has lasted near 6,000 years and, in its body, may be the eternal flames to torment the damned; and that was prepared from the foundation of the world for the devil and his angels and for all wicked men. Thus may we apprehend how the present state of the world shows us a possibility of all the changes of it described in the prophecies.

Since the first man was created immediately by God and that he has declared [that] he will raise men out of their graves, we can neither doubt of his power [n]or veracity. And he has described his method of doing that in Ezekiel: *The bones will come together, bone to his bone; . . . and the sinews and [the] flesh will come on theirs, and the skin covered them [above] . . . and the breath will enter into them, and they shall live* (Ch 37, v 7). These were the whole house of Israel who were slain (v 11), and the dry bones were shaked out of their graves: they must be one kingdom and have David for their king. None of this can happen till after the resurrection and therefore there is a description of it: all that is objected as difficult is our mistake about the same substantial particles. If they be not collected 'tis the same body. But, since all our parts are in continual flux and alteration, from our infancy to our death, we continually change the substantial particles and yet believe we are the same body, because we retain the same figure and actions. So if our bodies are made according to the same manner, figure, sense and actions we had when living, we shall believe we have the same body which is reunited to the same soul. And by the external figure and corporeal as well as spiritual actions, we shall be conscious that we are the same persons. Matter never sinned because [it is] insensible nor is capable of reward. Therefore organised matter is the body and, if the organs be the same, 'tis the same body. We can never discern the substantial particles of our bodies nor know when we change them. All our sensation is by our organs and if we find the same action of sense in them we believe we have the same bodies that is the same organised matter.

If the same organised body arises as [it] were in this life, then those who rise may live during the millenium and eat as our Saviour did after his resurrection. The angels' food, manna, is mentioned in the description of the state (Revelation Ch 2, v 17); and the marriage supper of the lamb and the tree of life to make their bodies immortal, which is in the midst of the paradise of God. *They will rule the nations with a rod of iron* (v 27); *he shall be clothed in white* (Ch 3, v 5); *have a new name and to sit in Christ's throne. I will come in to him and will sup with him and he with me.* (Revelation Ch 3, v 20). *The lamb which is in the midst of the throne shall feed them, and [shall] lead them unto living fountains of waters; and God shall wipe away all tears from their eyes* (Ch 7, v 17).

All these things may be literally interpreted and therefore are not symbolical. But when the just are removed into the new Heaven and new earth, the terrestrial bodies will be changed into the celestial. And, since in that state there can be no decay, all the inward viscera which were made for preparation of new nutriment will be changed; as St Paul says: *Meats for the belly, and [the] belly for meats; but God will destroy [both it and them]* (Corinthians I, Ch 6, v 13). And then there will remain an angelical body for the inhabitants of the new earth consisting of pipes filled with aethereal spirit, as our nerves are with the animal. And the pure aether will be the instrument of the soul for sensation and motion of the limbs. The soul thus being incorporated in a glorious angelical body and living amongst holy company in the earth and in the employment of angels, it will attain to its utmost felicity. The finest fluid as the aether, must be contained in some solid vessels, otherways it cannot represent the figure of a man or angel. A body being without figure or member is unconceivable; therefore the celestial body must have solid parts as well [as] fluid. And though it be objected that the angels suddenly disappear which a solid body cannot, yet I may say the same did our Saviour's body in which He appeared to His disciples before it was changed into His celestial glory.

Chapter 8

Devotions Made Out of Epictetus's Morals, and Simplicius's Comment (Fig. 51)[134]

O GOD OF ALL Nature who has given me a principle of reason as well as a body, and has taught me that [the] real essence of a man is his rational soul, who ought to make use of the body as its instrument and therefore Thou designest that I should have a life of reason and not be led by my senses, and that all my bodily passions should conform themselves to the commands of their lawful superior – and that all my fears and desires should be reduced into order, direct me in this inquiry, that I may examine human nature and consider its true condition and constitution, and what actions and sentiments are agreeable to this nature, and

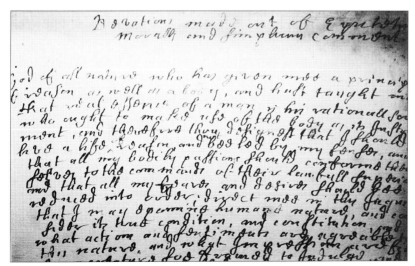

Fig. 51. *Beginning of Floyer's "Devotions Made Out of Epictetus's Morals, and Simplicius's Comment", the Library, The Queen's College, Oxford.*

what impressions are fit for a creature so framed to indulge, and what are to be stifled and restrained as incongruous and unseemly. Instruct me in all the diseases of the soul, and in the means and medicines proper for its recovery, and awaken my endeavours into a serious thought of a reformation.

Invigorate my rational soul that it may maintain its own dignity, and exert all its faculties in such operations as are agreeable to uncorrupt nature. Let my rational soul always preserve its own liberty, so as not to be enslaved to the body, or any of its sensual inclinations, but constantly raise itself above these, and aspire to the enjoyment of its proper happiness.

Give me those outward things which can any way conduce to the promoting of my real happiness, and give me the temper and moderation in the use of them. Give to my body that vigour and perfection which its nature is capable of to make it a fit instrument to be managed under the government of the soul, and as my body gathers new strength by exercise, and by repeating frequently those motions which are natural to it, so let my soul exert its power and by practice of such things as are agreeable to its nature, confirm itself in habits, and strengthen its own natural constitution.

I am now in that season of age that is most agreeable to virtue. The vehemences of youth are worn off and the weakness[es] of old age have not yet disabled me. My passions are more sedate and judgement solid. Now therefore excite me to take all the care and pains to be good, to conform all my actions to right reason, and to fix this as a perpetual and inviolable law, to retrench my desires, to allay all my passions, and to bring every inclination and aversion to fix on proper objects, and confine them within their just bounds, that I may now aspire to perfection and live as one that loves God.

Notes

1. For general biographical information on Floyer, see J.A. Gunn, "British Masters of Medicine: Sir John Floyer, 1649-1734", *Medical Press and Circular* (3 October 1934): 297-299; L. Lindsay, "Sir John Floyer (1649-1734)", *Proceedings of the Royal Society of Medicine* 44 (1951): 43-48; D. Gibbs, "Sir John Floyer (1649-1734)", *Transactions of the Johnson Society* (1968): 19-30; D. Gibbs, "Sir John Floyer, MD (1649-1734)", *British Medical Journal* 1 (1969): 242-245; Geoffrey Smerdon, "Four Seventeenth-Century Oxford Eccentrics", in K. Dewhurst (ed) *Oxford Medicine* (Oxford: Sanford, 1970), pp. 14-22; D.D. Gibbs, "Recommendations of Sir John Floyer on the Education of a Physician", *Proceedings of the XXIII Congress of the History of Medicine* 1 (2-9 September, 1972), 367-370; D.D. Gibbs, "Sir John Floyer, Dr Samuel Johnson and the Stanhope Family: Some Personal and Professional Links", *Transactions of the Johnson Society* (2001): 26-33; and D. Gibbs, "An Unhappy Household in Lichfield Cathedral Close in the Early 18th Century: Sir John Floyer's Second Marriage", *The Friends of Lichfield Cathedral Sixty-Eighth Annual Report* (2005): 23-30.
2. For further discussion of Wilkins, see Barbara Shapiro, *John Wilkins 1614-1723: An Intellectual Biography* (Berkeley: University of California Press, 1969).
3. For an extensive and scholarly perspective of the subject, see Robert G. Frank Jr., *Harvey and the Oxford Physiologists: A Study of Scientific Ideas* (Berkeley: University of California Press, 1980).
4. Michael Hunter provided an illustrative overview of this important individual in *Elias Ashmole: The Founder of the Ashmolean Museum and his World* (Oxford: Ashmolean Museum, 1983). See also Tobias Churton, *Magus: The Invisible Life of Elias Ashmole* (Lichfield: Signal Publishing, 2004).
5. For illuminating accounts of the display of these sports of nature, see Oliver Impey and Arthur MacGregor (eds), *The Origins of Museums: The Cabinet of Curiosities in Sixteenth and Seventeenth Century Europe* (Oxford: Clarendon, 1985); Lorraine Datson and Katherine Park, *Wonders and the Order of Nature* (New York: Zone Books, 1998); and Laura Lunger Knoppers and Joan B. Landes

(eds) *Monstrous Bodies Political Monstrosities in Early Modern Europe* (Ithaca: Cornell University Press, 2004).

6. Robert Plot, *De Origine Fontium, Tentamen Philosophicum. In Praelectione Habita Coram Societate Philosophica nuper Oxonii Instituta ad Scientiam Naturalem Promovendam* (Oxford: Sheldonian Theatre, 1684).

7. For further discussion of Botany in the university experience, see Christopher Wordsworth, *Scholae Academicae: Some account of the Studies at the English Universities in the Eighteenth Century* (Cambridge: Cambridge University Press, 1877), esp. pp. 202-212; R.H. Gunther, *Oxford Gardens, Based upon Daubeny's Popular Guide to the Physick Garden of Oxford* (Oxford: Parker & Son, 1912); and R.H. Gunther, *Early British Botanists and Their Gardens* (Oxford: Frederick Hall, 1922).

8. Sir D'Arcy Power, "The Oxford Physic Garden", *Annals of the History of Medicine*, 2 (1919): 109-125.

9. Edward Jorden (1569-1632), *A Discourse of Natural Bathes and Minerall Waters*, 3rd ed. revised & enlarged by Thomas Guidott (London: T. Salmon, 1669).

10. For a more complete discussion of hydrotherapy and cold bathing in Floyer's era, see Phyllis May Hembry, "Cold Bathing at the Minor Spas", *The English Spas, 1560-1815: A Social History* (London: Athlone, 1990), pp. 159-178; Keith Thomas, "Cleanliness and Godliness in Early Modern England", in A. Fletcher and P. Roberts (eds) *Religion, Culture & Society in Early Modern Britain* (Cambridge: Cambridge University Press, 1994), pp. 56-83; and Mark Jenner, "Bathing and Baptism: Sir John Floyer and the Politics of Cold Bathing", in K. Sharpe and S.N. Zwicken (eds) *Refiguring Revolutions: Aesthetics and Politics from the English Revolution to the Romantic Revolution* (Berkeley, California: University of California Press, 1998), pp. 19-216

11. It was on the same site that nearly a century later Dr Erasmus Darwin created his well-known botanic garden.

12. John Floyer, *The Ancient ΨΥΧΡΟΛΥΣΙΑ Revived; or, An Essay to Prove Cold Bathing both Safe and Useful. In Four Letters* (London: S. Smith and B. Walford, 1702), Letter IV, pp. 96-97.

13. Floyer provided a printed list of the titles of five manuscripts which he deposited in the Library of The Queen's College, Oxford, in *Medicina Gerocomica; or, The Galenic Art of Preserving Old Men's Health*, (London: J. Isted, 1724), verso of page 135. Paul Kaufman provided a timeless reminder of the importance of library collections in *Libraries and their Users: Collected Papers in Library History* (London: The Library Association, 1969). Regarding Kaufman's particular interest in Lichfield, see his "Readers and their Reading

in Eighteenth-Century Lichfield", *The Library* 5th ser 28 (1973): 108-115.

14. See E. Hobhouse, *The Library of a Physician circa 1700* (London: The Bibliographical Society, 1932), and E. Hobhouse, *The Diary of a West Country Physician* (London: S. Marshall, London, 1934).

15. For further discussion of Hewett, see Denis Gibbs, "Dr Anthony Hewett (*c.*1603-1684) MD Padua and Cambridge, Physician of Lichfield and Student of Renaissance Medicine", *Staffordshire Studies* 16(2005): 113-123.

16. Gabriele Falloppio, *De Medicatis Aquis Atque de Fossilibus* (Venice: J. Ziletti, 1564).

17. Andreas Cleyer, *Specimen Medicinae Sinicae* (Frankfort: J.P. Zubrodt, 1682).

18. B. Szczesniak, "John Floyer and Chinese Medicine", *Osiris* 11 (1954): 127-156; G.L. Townsend, "Sir John Floyer (1649-1734) and his Study of Pulse and Respiration", *Journal of the History of Medicine and Allied Sciences* 22 (1967): 286-316; and Linda L. Barnes, *Needles, Herbs, Gods, and Ghosts: China, Healing, and the West to 1848* (Cambridge: Harvard University Press, 2005), esp. pp. 72-125.

19. Available online at http://www.queens.ox.ac.uk/library/wellcometrust/docs/floyer-ms.html

20. Floyer compiled much of the material found in an additional unpublished manuscript in another repository, MS Lich 21 "Country Receipts" in The Cathedral Library, Lichfield Cathedral, Lichfield, Staffordshire.

21. John Evelyn, *Memoirs for my Grand-son*, transcribed by Geoffrey Keynes (Oxford: Nonesuch Press, 1926), p. 37.

22. Louis B. Wright (ed) *Advice to a Son: Precepts of Lord Burghley, Sir Walter Raleigh, and Francis Osborne* (Ithaca: Cornell University Press, 1962). See also Richard Lingard, *A Letter of Advice to a Young Gentleman Leaving the University, Concerning his Behaviour in the World* (London, 1671).

23. For an overview of this genre of works, see G. C. Brauer, *The Education of a Gentleman: Theories of Gentlemanly Education in England, 1660-1775* (New York: Bookman, 1959).

24. Daniel Waterland, *Advice to a Young Student, with a Method of Study for the Four First Years* (London: J. Crownfield, 1730), Advertisement. For a contemporary work set in Cambridge, see Ambrose Bonwicke, *A Pattern for Young Students in the University* (London: J. and J. Bonwicke, S. Austen, and F. Cogan, 1729).

25. Patrick Romanell, "The Significance of Locke's *De Arte Medica*", *Memorias del XIII Congresso Internacional de Filosoféa* 13 (1964), 7:127-133; Théophile Bonet, *A Guide to the Practical Physician:*

Shewing from the most Approved Authors, both Ancient and Modern, the Truest and Safest way of Curing all Diseases . . . To which is added, an Appendix Concerning the Office of a Physician (London: T. Flesher, 1684); Samuel Parker, *An Essay upon the Duty of Physicians and Patients, the Dignity of Medicine, and the Prudentials of Practice* (London: J.G. for H. Clements, 1715); Joannes Groenevelt, *The Rudiments of Physick Clearly and Accurately Describ'd and Explained* (Sherborne: R. Goadby and London: W. Owen,1753); and John Gregory, *Lectures on the Duties and Qualifications of a Physician,* new edition, (London: W. Strahan and T. Cadell, 1772.) Not to be forgotten is the exchange on medical education between Sir Thomas Browne and his young friend, Henry Power; an exchange documented in Geoffrey Keynes (ed) *The Works of Sir Thomas Browne* (London: Faber and Faber, 1964), Volume 6, Letters 172-172, pp. 255-264. An unpublished mid-Seventeenth-Century manuscript, "Advyse to a Young Physician. To One who Intends to Studie Medicine and Live Thereby", is among the British Library's Sloane manuscripts, MS 163, fols. 2-3. On medical education itself during this period, see Christopher Wordsworth, *Scholae Academicae: Some Account of the Studies at the English Universities in the Eighteenth Century* (Cambridge: Cambridge University Press, 1877), esp. pp. 171-186, and for medical education at Oxford in particular, A.H.T. Robb-Smith, "Medical Education at Oxford and Cambridge Prior to 1850", in F.N.L. Poynter (ed) *The Evolution of Medical Education in Britain* (London: Pitman, 1966), pp. 19-52; and H.M. Sinclair, "Oxford Medicine", in Allen G. Debus (ed) *Medicine in Seventeenth Century England* (Berkeley: University of California Press, 1974), pp. 371-391. For a contemporary view of Oxford University education at the time Floyer wrote his *Advice,* see W. H. Quarrell and W.J.C. Quarrell, *Oxford in 1710 from the Travels of Zacharias Conrad von Uffenbach* (Oxford: Basil Blackwell, 1928).

26. J. Groenevelt, *The Rudiments of Physick* (1754 edition), preface, i. For an exemplary biographical study of Groenevelt, see Harold J. Cook, *Trials of an Ordinary Doctor: Joannes Groenevelt in Seventeenth-Century London* (Baltimore: The Johns Hopkins University Press, 1994).

27. Parenthetical page references are drawn from Floyer MS. 558 entitled *Advise to a Young Student in Physicke.* We have adopted the spelling of *Advice* rather than *Advise* throughout this work in an attempt to make consistent and conventional a word that Floyer spelled both ways from time to time. John Bellers (1654-1725) produced similar arguments for the advancement of medical education via hospitals and a College of Physicians in the twelve proposals he enumerated in his 1714 "Essay Towards the Improvement of

Physic," a work reprinted in George Clarke (ed) *John Bellers: His Life, Times and Writings* (London: Routledge & Kegan Paul, 1987), pp. 174-220.

28. Christopher Wordsworth, *Scholae Academicae: Some Account of the Studies at the English Universities in the Eighteenth Century* (Cambridge: Cambridge University Press, 1877), p. 171.

29. For more on the Galenists, see Owsei Temkin, *Galenism: Rise and Decline of a Medical Philosophy* (Ithaca: Cornell University Press, 1973) and specifically for Floyer's period, Lester S. King, "The Transformation of Galenism", in Allen G. Debus (ed) *Medicine in Seventeenth Century England* (Berkeley: University of California Press, 1974), pp. 7-31. Brian K. Nance provided a stimulating synthesis of how physicians, in Galenic fashion, drew upon theory and signs to formulate opinions about a patient's entire temperament in "Determining the Patient's Temperament: An Excursion into Seventeenth-Century Medical Semeiology", *Bulletin of the History of Medicine* 67 (1993): 417-438. Andrew Wear has provided the most probing and thorough synthesis of the shaping of medical thought and practice during Floyer's day as well as the context within which the medicine he knew was derived, in *Knowledge & Practice in English Medicine, 1550-1680* (Cambridge: Cambridge University Press, 2000).

30. John Floyer, *Medicina Gerocomica* (1724), preface.

31. Allen G. Debus provided a comparative overview of various English iatrochemical proponents in *The English Paracelsians* (London: Oldbourne, 1965). See also Debus's *Chemistry, Alchemy and the New Philosophy 1550-1700* (London: Variorum Reprints, 1987).

32. Robert T. Gunther, *Early Science in Oxford* (Oxford: Printed for the Subscribers, 1925) Vol. I, p. 310. R.G. Frank also provided a glimpse into chymistry lectures during Floyer's period in his "The John Ward Diaries, Mirror of Seventeenth Century Science and Medicine", *Journal of the History of Medicine*, 29 (1974): 147-179. In this work, Frank describes how John Ward (1629-1681), vicar of Stratford-on-Avon, on his annual visit to Oxford, attended a "cursus chymicus" in 1667/68. Ward kept a notebook with details of laboratory protocols, comments on the use of chemical apparatus, and gossip about the chemists of Oxford. The procedures he described included a good cross-section of available laboratory techniques: destructive and fractional distillation, calcination, purification by sublimation, filtration, alcohol extraction, and precipitation.

33. L. J. Rather, "Some Relations between Eighteenth-Century Fibre Theory and Nineteenth-Century Cell Theory", *Clio Medica* 4 (1969): 191-202. Another brief discussion of fibres, drawn from one of Floyer's contemporaries, also exemplifies the iatromechani-

cal images common during this period. "The elasticity of a fibre, by which it recoils and crispates to any degree after its forceful dilatation, or upon stimulations, is the cause of many phoenomena in Nature. In us it is diminished, or encreased; by its diminution, our blood ceases to move forward; and by its encrease, the vessels are straightened, and the blood's circulation is also disturbed. Glass itself, like our fibres, contracts by coldness, and dilates by heat, and both compress the liquors contained thereby; and many disorders arise from either, but health is preserved by a due degree of it: it arises from motion implanted in a fibre, after it is stretched to its full pitch: it is a property implanted by the Almighty in a fibre, of which we can give no account, but we know it is preserved by stimulation, by cold externally, or hot medicines internally, by absorption of excessive humidity, with moderate fire, or absorbents; by an external body equally compressing, *viz.* by immersion in water with discharges (by bleeding, catharticks, &c.) and the fibres become too rigid by any permanent stimulation". Edward Strother, *Materia Medica; or, A New Description of the Virtues and Effects of all Drugs, or Simple Medicines Now in Use*, Second edition (London: C. Rivington, 1721), Vol. 1, A General Introduction, p. liii.

34. A. Sakula, "Sir John Floyer's *A Treatise of the Asthma* (1698)", *Thorax* 39 (1984): 248-254.

35. D.D. Gibbs, "The Physician's Pulse Watch", *Medical History* 15 (1971): 187-190, and D. Gibbs, "Pusilogium to Pulse Watch", *Proceedings of the 39th International Congress on the History of Medicine*, 3 (Bari: Progedit, 2006): 97-100. For discussion of the importance of Floyer's Lichfield to this work, see D. Gibbs, " The Almshouses of Lichfield: Cradles of Pulse-timing", *Journal of Medical Biography* 2 (1994): 89-93. For a more general appreciation of instrumental precision and medicine, see S. Weir Mitchell, *The Early History of Instrumental Precision in Medicine* (New Haven; Tuttle, Moorehouse & Taylor, 1892), and E. Ashworth Underwood, "The History of the Quantitative Approach in Medicine", *British Medical Bulletin* 7 (1951): 261-264.

36. J.F. Hayward, *English Watches,* Victoria and Albert Museum (London: HMSO 1969).

37. Santorio Santorio [Sanctorius], *Commentaria in Primam fen Primi Libri Canonis Avicennae* (Venetiis: J. Sarcina, 1626).

38. Several such books are discussed in Lucinda M. Beier, *Sufferers and Healers: The Experience of Illness in 17th-Century England* (London: Routledge, 1987), and in Roy Porter (ed.) *The History of Medical Popularization* (London: Routledge, 1992).

39. Harold J. Cook, "The New Philosophy and Medicine in Seventeenth-Century England", in D.C. Lindberg and R.S.

Westman (eds), *Reappraisals of the Scientific Revolution* (Cambridge University Press, 1990), pp. 398-399.

40. For a recent overview of the use of Hippocratic wisdom in Floyer's era, see David Cantor (cd.), *Reinventing Hippocrates* (Aldershot: Ashgate 2002).

41. For further discussion of the importance of the physician's use of senses, see W.F. Bynum and Roy Porter (eds) *Medicine and the Five Senses* (Cambridge: Cambridge University Press, 1993).

42. Nehemiah Grew, *The Anatomy of Plants. With an Idea of a Philosophical History of Plants, and Several Other Lectures Read before the Royal Society* (London: W. Rawlins, 1682). William R. LeFanu provided a textual analysis of Grew's works in *Nehemiah Grew: A Study and Bibliography of His Writings* (Winchester: St Paul's Biographies, 1990).

43. John Floyer, *The Touch-stone of Medicines* (1687), preface.

44. John Floyer, *The Touch-stone of Medicines* (1687), preface.

45. John Floyer, *The Touch-stone of Medicines* (1687), preface.

46. For a helpful insight into the breadth and significance of biblical metaphor in the writings and teaching at the Oxford Floyer experienced, see Jim Bennett and Scott Mandelbrote, *The Garden, the Ark, the Tower, the Temple: Biblical Metaphors of Knowledge in Early Modern Europe* (Oxford: Museum of the History of Science in association with the Bodleian Library, 1998).

47. John Ray, *The Wisdom of God Manifested in the Works of Creation* (London: W. Innis, 1691). For a thorough discussion of Ray's contributions, see Charles E. Raven, with an Introduction by S.M. Walters, *John Ray: His Life and Works* (Cambridge: Cambridge University Press, 1986).

48. For a thorough overview of this aspect of Newton, see F.E. Manuel, *The Religion of Isaac Newton* (Oxford: Clarendon Press, 1974).

49. Terence (*c.*190-*c.*159 BC), a Roman comic poet born in Carthage, was considered a suitable author for study by English schoolboys because of his choice of language and purity of Latin when presenting his themes in the comedy of manners. The *Comedies of Terence* were considered very suitable for furnishing good expression in Latin speaking.

50. Desiderius Erasmus (*c.*1446-1536), among the greatest humanists of the Renaissance, wrote the *Colloquies* first as formulae of polite address, and later expanded into lively conversations that in his view, made "better Latinists and better characters of schoolboys".

51. The *Colloquies* of Corderius (*c.*1480-1564), like those of Erasmus, were used in schools for at least three centuries. After the Restoration, the practice of speaking Latin in school had diminished.

52. Jean Le Clerc (1657-1736), *Physica; sive, De Rebus Corporeis Libri Quinque, in Quibus, Praemissis Potissimis Corporearum Naturarum Phaenomenis & Proprietatibus, Veterum & Recentiorum de Eorum Causis Celeberrimae Conjecturae Traduntur* (Amsterdam: G. Gallet, 1696).

53. Nicolas Lemery (1645-1715) popularised chemistry within medical education and practice primarily through his successful textbook translated from the French into English by the Oxford educated physician, James Keill (1673-1719), as *A Course of Chymistry, Containing an Easy Method of Preparing those Chymical Medicines which are Used in Physic* (London: W. Kettilby, 1677).

54. James Drake (1667-1707), *Anthropologia Nova; or, A New System of Anatomy* (London: S. Smith and B.J. Walford, 1707).

55. Incorporation by the Universities of Oxford or Cambridge of a medical degree obtained abroad could enable a graduate in medicine (physic), in due course, to become a Candidate and then a Fellow of the Royal College of Physicians.

56. George Bate (1608-1669), *Pharmacopoeia Bateana; or, Bate's Dispensatory* (London: S. Smith and B. Walford, 1694). Remarkably, Bate was successively physician to Charles I, Oliver Cromwell and Charles II. His formulae and recipes were published posthumously by the apothecary James Shipton.

57. Thomas Fuller (1654-1734), *Pharmacopoeia Extemporanea; or, A Body of Prescripts* (London: B. Walford, 1710).

58. John Floyer, *The Preternatural State of the Animal Humours Described by their Sensible Qualities, which Depend on the Different Degrees of their Fermentation. And the Cure of each Particular Cacochymia is Performed by Medicines of a Specific Taste, Described* (London: M. Johnson, 1696).

59. Lazare Riviére [Riverius] (1589-1655) expounded upon the theoretical background of medicine in his last major work, *The Practice of Physick* (London: P. Cole, 1655). In this work, he provided an extensive summary of Galenic teaching presented in a traditional framework with five-fold divisions: physiology, pathology, semeiotics (i.e. the study of symptoms and signs), hygiene and therapeutics.

60. Michael Ettmüller (1644-1683), *Etmullerus Abridg'd; or, A Complete System of the Theory and Practice of Physic* (London: E. Harris, F. Hubbard, and A. Bell, 1699). Ettmüller was a German iatrochemist who became Professor of Medicine in Leipzig. In 1668, when he was 24, he spent a year in Oxford, where he was influenced by Robert Boyle and was acquainted with Thomas Willis. In his lectures in Leipzig in the early 1680s, he cited the work of John Mayow and Boyle, showing that air was necessary for both fire and life. See

Robert G. Frank, *Harvey and the Oxford Physiologists: A Study of Scientific Ideas* (Berkeley: University of California Press, 1980). Floyer, five years younger than Ettmüller, was an undergraduate when Ettmüller visited Oxford.

61. Thomas Willis, P*ractice of Physic, Being the Whole Works of that Renowned and Famous Physician* (London: T. Dring, C. Harper, and J. Leigh, 1684). Floyer modelled his own views of practice primarily upon Willis' teachings.

62 . John Floyer, *A Treatise of the Asthma* (London: R. Wilkin, 1698).

63. Richard Morton's (1637-1698) D*e Febribus Inflammatoris*, the third book in his *Opera Medica* (Amsterdam: D. Donati, 1696).

64. Richard Lower (1631-1691), *Tractatus de Corde. Item de Motu et Calore Sanguinis et Chyli in eum Transitu* (London: J. Redmayne, 1669).

65. Edward Strother (1675-1737), *Criticon Febrium; or, A Critical Essay on Fevers.* (London: C. Rivington, 1716).

66. François de le Boë [Sylvius] (1614-1672), *A New Idea of the Practice of Physic* (London: B. Aylmer, 1675). Sylvius was an influential iatro-chemical physician.

67. Thomas Sydenham (1624-1689), *Practice of Physic* (London: S. Smith, B. Walford, and J. Knapton, 1695). Sydenham's special contribution was to revive Hippocratic reliance on clinical observation and experience. He wrote in English and had his works translated into Latin for publication; subsequent translators were quick to present them again in English.

68. The extent to which the student, even "upon long practice", would have been expected to familiarise himself with the formidable array of collected works of Hippocrates and of Galen, is not clear. The title and contents of one such collection (13 volumes in 9, containing more than 8000 pages), with Greek and Latin in parallel columns, is given as an example of a compendium which could have been consulted in the student's College library. *Hippocrates Coi, et Claudii Galeni . . . Opera* (Paris: A. Pralard, 1679). In Floyer's bequest to The Queen's College were two extracts from Hippocrates: *Aphorisimi Novi, ex Hippocrtis Operibus . . . Collecti* (Annissonni Lugduni: J. Posnel and C. Rigand, 1684) and *Hippocrates, de Morbis Popularibus*, with a new commentary on fevers provided by John Freind (London: W. Innys, 1717).

69. Pieter van Foreest [Forestus] (1522-1597), *Observationum et Curationum Medicinalium ac Chirurgicarum, Opera Omnia* (Frankfurt: Collegi Musarum Paltheniano, 1631). A Dutch physician, who practised for many years at Alkmaar and later at Delft. He studied medicine in Italy and was a pupil of Vesalius. He began

publishing his *Observationes et Curationes* series in 1588 and, at the time of his death, the series on diseases comprised 32 books.

70. Daniel Sennert [Sennertus] (1572-1637), *Practical Physick* (London: W. Whitwood, 1679). The *Institute's* of Riverius and Sennert are remarkably similar in content and arrangement. In both, the authors first deal with the study of nature, especially nature as it pertains to the functions of man, describing seven specific aspects, the so-called "naturals", the "res naturales", or things according to nature. The seven "naturals" comprise the elements, the temperaments, the humours, the spirits and natural heat, the parts, the faculties and functions and finally, the generation of man.

71. The recommendation by Floyer is revealing, showing that, after a long university training in medicine, a young physician aspiring to start practice in a provincial town should be prepared to offer expertise in surgery and midwifery. For such a role he advocated first equipping himself by spending some time in hospitals abroad, in France or Holland. After several years in practice he would presumably have become sufficiently established and secure financially to allow him to confine his practice to physic. For example, in two counties adjoining Staffordshire, where Floyer practised, James Cooke (1614-?1688) of Warwick, was a surgeon who was also involved in midwifery, and Francis Willughby (1596-1685), who trained in Oxford in physic and then practised in Derby, had an extensive practice in midwifery.

72. A chalebeate spring produced waters impregnated or flavoured with iron.

73. In pursuing the "introductory or ornamental parts", Floyer supported the need for students to study these subjects, but was concerned that, once in practice, "he cannot be a good physician who employs all his time" (53). His concern was that excessive enthusiasm for such subjects would prompt the physician to become a virtuoso who might be diverted from the full commitment and dedication required of a physician to his patients and to his art.

74. A "simple" was considered to be an individual herb or a single ingredient in a medicine. By contrast, an extemporaneous form of medicine contained several ingredients, usually prepared by an apothecary.

75. Eusebius (263-339) of Caesarea was one of the most voluminous writers of antiquity. Floyer and his contemporaries continued to turn to the *History of the Christian Church* written in 324, the work to which Eusebius owed his lasting fame and the title of "the father of ecclesiastical history". Eusebius was a member of the Nicene Council when the Nicene Creed was agreed in 325. The Nicene

110

Creed remains among the most accepted and widely used concise statement of Christian faith.

76. Dioscorides (First Century AD) wrote in detail about the Mandragoras and referred to "another sort called Morion, growing in shady places . . . having leaves like to ye white mandrake . . . . For a man sleeps . . . sensible of nothing for 3 or 4 hours, from ye time that it is brought him. And Physitians also, use this, when they are about to cut, or cauterize". *The Greek Herbal of Dioscorides*, illustrated by a Byzantine A.D. 512. Englished by John Goodyer A.D. 1655. Edited and first printed A.D. 1933, by Robert T. Gunther (New York: Hafner Publishing Co., 1959), p. 474.

77. Fabrizio Bartoletti (1587-1630), Professor of Surgery and Anatomy in Bologna where he compiled the *Encyclopaedia Hermitico-Dogmatica* (Bologna: S. Bobomium, 1619). Floyer acquired this work from Dr Anthony Hewett. The mental effects of the thorn apple (*Datura stramonium*) had long been known. Dioscorides referred to "the root being drank with wine ye quantity of a dragm, hath ye power to effect not unpleasant fantasies". (R.T. Gunther, *The Greek Herbal of Dioscorides*), p. 470.

78. In the Second Epistle to the Corinthians, Ch 12, v 7, St Paul wrote that "there was given to me a thorn in the flesh, the messenger of Satan to buffet me, lest I should be exalted above measure". St Paul's infirmity was probably migraine.

79. In 1736, William Hogarth commemorated *The Pool of Bethesda* in a mural in the staircase entrance to the Great Hall of St Bartholomew's Hospital in London.

80. Pausanias, a Greek traveller and geographer of the 2nd century AD, noted that "A Roman senator, Antoninus, made in our own day a bath of Aesclepius with a sanctuary of the gods. He made also a temple to Health, Aesclepius and Apollo". (Pausanias 2.27.6) The medical historian, Arturo Castiglione relates that as a reward for curing Augustus Caesar with cold baths, Antonius Musa had his statue erected beside that of Aesculapius. Of related interest, *Aqua Solis* is discussed at length in William Burton, *A Commentary on Antoninus his Itinerary or Journies of the Romane Empire so far as it Concerneth Britain* (London: T. Roycroft for H. Twyford and T. Twyford, 1658). Floyer noted another Roman attribute to Aesculapius regarding the physician, Antonius Musa, in his *Cold Baths*.

81. Peruvian bark, widely known in Floyer's time, was featured in Sir Robert Talbor's *The English Remedy; or, Talbor's Wonderful Secret, for Cureing of Agues, Feavers, ...* (London: J. Wallis, for J. Hindmarsh, 1682).

82. Galen was born in A.D. 129 in Pergamum, the son of an architect. Galen's father oversaw his son's learning, encouraging him to combine the study of medicine with the study of philosophy. Upon his father's death in A.D. 148/149, Galen left to study in Smyrna, Corinth, and Alexandria where he became well acquainted with the philosophical schools of Platonism, Aristotelianism, Epicureanism, and Stoicism.

83. Hippocrates, (B.C. 460-377), of Cos, was commonly referred to as "Hippocrates Asclepiades", implying his descent from a family of physicians. Among his teachers of medicine was his father, Heracleides.

84. For a detailed consideration of "the three great professions", the church, law, and medicine, during the time of Floyer, see Geoffrey Holmes, *Augustan England – Professions, State and Society, 1680-1730* (London: George Allan and Unwin, 1982), especially pp. 81-235.

85. For an overview of Galen's' emphasis on the importance of philosophy for physicians, see Albert Z. Iskandar (trans.), *On Examinations by Which the Best Physicians Are Recognized* (Berlin: Akademie, 1988), and selections from Arthur J. Brock, *Greek Medicine, Being Extracts Illustrative of Medical Writers from Hippocrates to Galen* (London: J.M. Dent, 1929, reprinted 1977). For an important contextualization of Galen among the Ancients, see Vivian Nutton, *Ancient Medicine* (London: Routledge, 2004).

86. Hippocrates explained to his son that geometry is important in order to know the relative positions of bones so that they can be put right when they are twisted or fractured, and that arithmetic was crucial in order to be able to count days between changes in fever and other practical matters. Hippocrates, *Pseudepigraphic Writings: Letters, Embassy Speech from the Alter, Decree*. Edited and Translated with an Introduction by Wesley D. Smith, *Studies in Ancient Medicine*, 2 (Leiden: E.J. Brill, 1990), Letter 22.

87. According to J.F. Payne, "History" section of "Medicine" entry, *Encyclopaedia Britannica*, 9th ed, Vol. XV (London: A & C Black, 1879), p. 800, the "times at which crises were to be expected were naturally looked for with anxiety; and it was a cardinal point in the Hippocratic system to foretell them with precision. Hippocrates, influenced as is thought by the Pythagorean doctrine of numbers, taught that they were to be expected on days fixed by certain numerical rules, in some cases on odd, in others on even numbers—the celebrated doctrine of 'critical days'".

88. Astrology had lost much of its significance in medical prognostics in English medicine by Floyer's time. See, for example, Keith V. Thomas, *Religion and the Decline of Magic: Studies in Popular Beliefs*

in Sixteenth and Seventeenth Century England (London: Weidenfeld and Nicolson, 1971).

89. Chrysippus, head of the Stoic school, consolidated the teaching of logic and cultivated the use of the dialectical method.

90. Pythagoras of Samos (*c.*569-475 BC) and his followers believed that five concentric spheres surrounded the earth to which the planets and the stars were attached. When the spheres rotated, they created the wondrous musical "harmony of the spheres". Pythagoras was well known to another prominent Lichfield resident, William Lloyd (1627-1717). Lloyd, the Bishop of Lichfield and Coventry from 1692-1699 and a friend of Floyer, wrote *A Chronological Account of the Life of Pythagoras* (London: H. Mortlick and J. Hartley, 1699).

91. Demosthenes (384-322 AD) overcame his stammer by talking with pebbles in his mouth and strengthened his voice by speaking over the roar of the waves. Eventually, he became Greece's greatest orator, making eloquent, though futile, appeals for his countrymen to unite against King Philip of Macedon (in a style that became known as philippics) to preserve their freedom.

92. A term which, in Floyer's time, referred to the philosophical and experimental investigations into nature.

93. In medical education, the "Institutes" referred to the theoretical foundation in contrast to the practical (later known as the clinical) aspects of training.

94. René Descartes [Cartesius] (1596-1650), had become widely known during Floyer's time for his belief that space was entirely filled with material particles, whirling in a vortex pattern. According to the vortex theory, collisions of these particles provided ample force for pushing planets around the sun. Newton would later challenge this view, but Cartesius' belief held adherents, particularly in France, throughout the Enlightenment. Lucretius (99-55 BC) in his *De Rerum Natura* (*On the Nature of the Universe*) popularized an Epicurean world-view of matter as composed of imperishable atoms, tiny indivisible particles that can neither be created nor destroyed, a view dating back to Democritus (460-370 BC). Epicurus (*c.*341-271 BC) deviated from Democritus in regard to the natural motion of atoms. For Epicurus, atoms travelled downward with a uniform high velocity until, at random and unpredictable moments, they "swerve" from their course, colliding by chance with other atoms. Lucretius extended this materialistic atomic action as evidence for the existence of free will, a belief that was reinforced by the revival of Epicurean thought in the seventeenth century.

95. Floyer was well acquainted with acupuncture as described in Andreas Cleyer's *Specimen Medicinae Sinicae* (1682).

96. Baglivi, a founder of Italy's iatromechanical school, regarded the human body as a complicated piece of machinery. He is best remembered for his *De Praxi Medica ad Priscam Observandi Rationem Revocandi* (Rome: D.A. Herculis, 1696), which was translated into English as *The Practice of Physic Reduced to the Ancient Way of Observations, Concerning a Just Parallel between the Wisdom and Experience of the Ancients and the Hypotheses of Modern Physicians* (London: A Bell, R. Smith, D. Midwinter, T. Leigh, W. Hawes, W. Davis, G. Strahan, B. Lintott, J. Round, and J. Wale, 1704). Baglivi urged his students to visit the "publick hospitals and nasty beds of the sick . . . with an austere fearless patience". Like Thomas Sydenham, he considered the study of the patient to be more important than that of books, in acknowledging, "Let the young know that they will never find a more interesting, more instructive book than the patient himself".

97. Bonet's *Sepulchretum sive Anatomia Practica* (Geneva: L.Chouët, 1679) is the greatest of the *specilegia* or assemblages of necropsy reports, with nearly 3000 cases culled from literature dating back to Hippocrates, but drawing mainly upon sixteenth and seventeenth century cases.

98. W.N. Hargreaves-Mawdsley documents the Oxford curriculum at this time in his *Oxford in the Age of John Locke* (Norman, OK: University of Oklahoma Press, 1973).

99. For example, Thomas Willis, *Pharmaceutice Rationalis; or, An Exercitation of the Operations of Medicines in Humane Bodies* (London: T. Dring, C. Harper, and J. Leigh, 1679).

100. John Quincy (d. 1722) *Pharmacopoeia Officianalis & Extemporanea; or, A Complete English Dispensatory* (London: A. Bell, W. Taylor, and J. Osborn, 1719). The physician Peter Shaw (1694-1764) described Quincy's work as an "unparallel'd performance"; fifteen subsequent editions, the last in 1782, confirm its popularity and success. Quincy published separately an edited translation from the Latin of the *London Pharmacopoeia* as *The Dispensatory of the Royal College of Physicians in London* (London: W. Bower for R. Knaplock, B. Took, D. Midwinter, R. Smith, W. and J. Innys, and J. Osborn, 1721) and, the year after Quincy's death, Shaw published *Praelectiones Pharmaceuticae; or, A Course of Lectures in Pharmacy* (London: E. Bell, J. Sennex, W. Taylor, W. and J. Innys, and J. Osborn, 1723).

101. Boyle, *Medicinal Experiments; or, A Collection of Choice and Safe Remedies*, 4th ed (London: S. Smith and J. Taylor, 1703). *Medicinal Experiments* first appeared in 1692 and passed eventually into three volumes and many editions. John F. Fulton in a *Bibliography of the Honourable Robert Boyle, Fellow of the Royal Society*, 2nd ed (Oxford:

114

Clarendon Press, 1961) made comments on the work which nowadays might be considered to have a "presentist" bias: "There are numerous statements in this astonishing collection of nostrums which shatter one's confidence in Boyle's judgment, but in charitableness it is better to regard the volume as a sad commentary upon the state of medicine in the seventeenth century rather that a reflection upon the integrity of a high-minded searcher after truth". There is no doubting the authenticity of Boyle's collection of choice and safe remedies, but they were collected for publication for the profit of others after Boyle's death, a practice common following the deaths of prominent personages of the period.

102. Dioscorides (First Century AD), *Amati Lusitani . . . In Dioscoridis Anazarbei: De Medica Materia Libris Quinque Enarrationes Eradutissimae* (Venice: I. Zilleti, 1757). Amatus Lusitanus (1511-1568) edited this edition of Dioscorides' *Materia Medica*, a copy of which Floyer acquired from Anthony Hewitt.

103. Ray, *Historia Plantarum* (London: M. Clark for H. Faithorne and J. Kersey, Vol. I, 1686; Vol. II, 1688). In these two volumes, Ray gave a comprehensive analysis of botanical knowledge of the time, with descriptions of over 18,800 plants classified under a new system he had developed; English and exotic plants were considered as well as some from the Americas and East Indies. Ray's earlier botanical study of the flora of Cambridgeshire, *Catalogus Plantarum circa Cantabrigiam Nascentium*, (Cambridge: W. Nealand, 1660), the first detailed botanical survey of a county, remains a landmark in the history of botany.

104. Pierre Pomet (1659-1699) *A Compleat History of Druggs . . . Done into English* [by Joseph Browne] (London: R. Bonwicke, W. Freeman, T. Goodwin, J. Walthoe, M. Wotton, S. Manship, J. Nicholson, B. Tooke, R. Parker, and R. Smith, 1712). This book is considered to be the first important materia medica to be published in English, being translated from the French original of 1694. Pomet was a renowned and well-travelled botanist, chemist and druggist, the proprietor of a "drug-house" in Paris and a teacher of botany in the *Jardin des Plantes*. The translator was anonymous and his identity, as Dr Joseph Browne (1673-*c*.1722), was only recently discovered. Floyer was acquainted with Browne who, in one of his many controversial publications, *The Modern Practice of Physick Vindicated* (London: N. Cox, 1703), dedicated *An Appendix in a Letter to the Learned Sir John Floyer about the Further Use of Cold Baths*. A few years later, Browne wrote another book on the same subject, a copy of which was owned by Floyer: *An Account of the Wonderful Cures Perform'd by the Cold Baths* (London: J. How, R. Borough, and J. Baker, 1707).

105. Paracelsus (1493-1541), extending the work of earlier alchemists, imparted a new emphasis on iatrochemical medicine that greatly influenced Boyle, among others in Oxford. However, Paracelsus – the "Luther of Medicine" – is typically more remembered for stirring considerable controversy regarding his aim to reform theoretical medicine from a Galenist humoural tradition towards one that viewed humans and the greater world in terms of microcosmic-macrocosmic analogies.

106. For further discussion, see Alastair Hamilton, *The Apocryphal Apocalypse: The Reception of the Second Book of Esdras (4 Ezra) from the Renaissance to the Enlightenment* (Oxford: Oxford University Press, 1999), esp. pp. 279-284.

107. One of Floyer's contemporaries, the London surgeon and physician Daniel Turner (1667-1741) drew attention to the well-polished ploys and tactics of medical quacks in his *The Modern Quack, or Medicinal Imposter* (London: J. Roberts, 1719). For more on Turner and quackery, see Philip K. Wilson, *Surgery, Skin, and Syphilis: Daniel Turner's London (1667-1741)* (Amsterdam: Rodopi, 1999), esp. pp. 85-111.

108. Robert Burton (1577-1640), who had been educated as a boy in Sutton Coldfield and Nuneaton and who later lived in Oxford, prepared, under the pseudonym Democritus Junior, a widely influential book on this subject, *The Anatomy of Melancholy* (Oxford: J. Lichfield and J. Short for H. Cripps, 1621).

109. Georg Wolfgang Wedel [Wedelius] (1645-1721) served on the medical faculty of Jena where he taught anatomy, theoretical medicine, practical medicine and chemistry. His iatrochemical interests were prominent, yet, at times, he retained astrological beliefs and defended alchemy. He influenced many physicians, including Friedrich Hoffmann (1626-1675) and Georg Ernst Stahl (1660-1734), and was a prolific author. Floyer owned a collection of Wedelius's dissertations, *De Medicamentorum Compositione Extemporanea, ad Praxim Clinicam & Usum Hodierrnum Accomodata* (Jena: J. Bielkii, 1679). Wedelius became more widely known in England after 1685 when *An Introduction to the Whole Practice of Physick* (London: W. Thackery and T. Teate) was published.

110. Gaius Plinius Secundus, known as Pliny the Elder (A.D. 23-79), was born in Como, Italy. In AD 77, he published the work for which he remains best known, a 37-volume encyclopaedic *Historia Naturalis* in which he "set forth in detail all the contents of the entire world", including fact and folklore.

111. Erasistratus of Chios (*c.*304-*c.*250 BC), learned the practice of medicine in Athens and served as court physician to one of Alexander the Great's successors, Seleucus Nicator (*c.*358-281 BC)

King of Syria. Moving to Alexandria, he founded a school of medicine. There, like his predecessor Herophilus (*c*.335-280 BC), he gained considerable insight into human form and function, especially involving cranial, vascular, and digestive regions, through human dissection and experimentation, and possibly vivisection.

112. This fee for a house call was fifteen times the going rate. The patient was the wife of the Roman consul Flavius Boethius, not to be confused with the philosopher, poet, and politician Boethius (*c*.480-524 CE), best known for his influential writing, *Consolation of Philosophy*.

113. Jody Rubin Pinault, in *Hippocratic Lives and Legends* (Leiden: Brill, 1992), examines the ideal of the ancient physician and the biographical fiction that shaped the legend of Hippocrates over time. One story that Pinault traces is Hippocrates' refusal to serve Artaxerxes, King of Persia.

114. These points are addressed in the Hippocratic Oath. For an overview of the origins and meanings contained within the oath, see Ludwig Edelstein, "The Hippocratic Oath: Text, Translation and Interpretation", in O. Temkin and C.L. Temkin (eds). *Ancient Medicine: Selected Papers of Ludwig Edelstein* (Baltimore: Johns Hopkins University Press, 1967), pp. 3-64.

115. In Roman mythology Diana, Goddess of the moon and of the hunt, was guardian of springs and streams and the protector of wild animals. She was also Goddess of fertility, who was believed to ease pain during childbirth.

116. For centuries, many Christians claimed that bloodstone, a form of Jasper, carried healing power due to markings that represented Christ's blood. Soldiers took bloodstone into battle for protection, for courage and to stop bleeding. Women carried bloodstone to ease menstrual difficulties and to diminish labour pain. Other stones that resembled serpents or were thought to be produced by toads were widely marketed for their healing powers. For an overview of the use of healing amulets in Floyers's era, see Martha Baldwin, "Toads and Plague: Amulet Therapy in Seventeenth-Century Medicine", *Bulletin of the History of Medicine* 67 (1993): 227-247

117. Theophrastus (371-286 BC) of Lesbos, a pupil of Plato and Aristotle, succeeded Aristotle as head of the Lyceum at Athens where he also oversaw the botanical garden. Theophrastus remains known mainly for botanical writings, *De Historia Plantarum (A History of Plants)* and *De Causis Plantarum (About the Reasons for Vegetable Growth)*.

118. Marcus Porcius Cato (234-149 BC) of Tusculum near Rome, spent his youth on his father's farm. He remains best known for his only surviving work, a farmer's journal or commonplace book, *De Agri*

Cultura, also published as *De re Rustica.* In this work, Cato noted the folk wisdom that incantations could magically heal dislocated limbs or broken bones.

119. Quintus Serenus Sammonicus (*fl.*240), a Gnostic physician, travelled with the Roman Emperor Septimus Severus to Britain in 208 AD. He compiled extensive material about natural history and the healing arts in his noted poem, *De Medicina Praecepta Saluberrima* (Paris: S. Colinaeum, 1533). Included in this poem is a discussion of the use of Abracadabra as an amulet against agues.

120. Floyer's view is consistent with that of his contemporary, Robert Boyle, who rejected belief in the materialistic notion of atomism – a key component to the seventeenth-century revival of Epicureanism – deeming that to support such philosophical tenets was akin to atheism. For further discussion, see J.J. MacIntosh, "Robert Boyle on Epicurean Atheism and Atomism", in M. Osler (ed) *Epicurean and Stoic Themes in European Thought* (Cambridge: Cambridge University Press, 1991), pp. 197-219.

121. Henricus Cornelius Agrippa (1486-1535), a sceptical philosopher known principally for his writings on occult philosophy and geomancy, but also for *The Vanity of Arts and Sciences* (London: J.C. for S. Speed, 1676).

122. Michel Eyquem de Montaigne (1533-1592), as a philosopher, forced a reconsideration of some fundamental aspects of Western thinking, including the superiority of man to animals and of European civilization over "barbarian" cultures. As a writer, he created the essay form in which he took himself as the object of his study, in attempt to "assay" his nature, habit, and opinions. This introspective study was, in essence, a study of all humanity. The poet and country squire Charles Cotton (1630-1687), born in Beresford, Staffordshire, translated Montaigne's *Essays* into English in a work that appeared in 1685 (London: T. Basset, M. Gilliflower, and W. Hensman).

123. Similar concerns were raised in the anonymous *Present State of Physick & Surgery in London* (London: T. Speed, 1701). For a broader contextualization of the struggles between these groups of practitioners as well as those with quacks in general, see Roy Porter's *Health for Sale: Quackery in England 1660-1850* (Manchester: Manchester University Press, 1989).

124. A druggist sold only drugs and medicines, but did not prepare them as did apothecaries.

125. A.W. Haggis, "Episcopal Medical Licences 1511-1829", Wellcome MS. 5328/1. The Act introduced a system the intention of which was to forbid physicians, surgeons, and midwives to practise without approval and licensing by Episcopal authorities. Not only were

candidates required to show evidence of moral rectitude, but oral examinations were carried out delegated to experienced local practitioners; graduates of Oxford and Cambridge were exempt. Variations in practice occurred in different parts of the country, and Floyer was commenting from his own experience and perspective.

126. A hot diet implied spicy foods as well as tea and coffee, and a high diet implied over indulgence.

127. Thomas Willis discussed how medicines, particularly externally applied medicines, were drawn to produce their effects upon particular inward parts via the process of "sympathetic attraction". For an in-depth multi-disciplinary perspective upon contemporary meanings of this term, see Patricia Fara, *Sympathetic Attractions: Magnetic Practices, Beliefs, and Symbolism in Eighteenth-Century England* (Princeton: Princeton University Press, 1996).

128. Floyer used Sir Samuel Morland's (1625-1695) hand-engine, a small pump which improved upon a syringe in introducing air into experiments. Morland, who applied his inventive talent and hydrostatic interests to pumps and pumping, had transferred the leather packing from the plunger to the barrel of his hand-engine. For further discussion, see H. W. Dickinson, *Sir Samuel Morland: Diplomat and Inventor, 1625-1695* (Cambridge: W. Heffer, 1970), esp. pp. 56-73.

129. In the epistle dedicatory of his *The Preternatural State of Animal Humours Described* (London: W. Downing for M. Johnson, 1696), Floyer acknowledged his debt to Sir Charles Holt (Fig. 43) of Aston Hall, Birmingham, for the extensive use of his microscopes; "by your microscopes, I have observed more of the consistenc[y] of fluids that I could otherwise have known".

130. Marcello Malpighi [Malpighius] (1628-1694) supported the preformationist doctrine that entire, preformed beings existed for all future generations within the reproductive structures of animals. In particular, as an ovist, Malpighi believed that these pre-formed entities preexisted in the egg. Ovists conjectured, according to Pomet's *A Compleat History of Druggs*, 3rd ed (London: J. and J. Bonwicke, R. Wilkin, S. Birt, T. Ward, and E. Wichsteed, 1737), preface, that "All animals . . . come from eggs, and are there enclosed, as it were in abridgement till the seed of the male penetrate their covering, and stretches them sufficiently that they are ready for hatching: there enters into their vessels a chylous juice, which being pushed forwards by the spirits, circulates through the whole habit of the little body, nourishes and dilates by little and little, which makes what we call growth". For Malpighi's influential articulation of ovists' views, see his *Dissertatio Epistolica de Formatione Pulli in Ovo* (London: J. Martin, 1673). Antonie van Leeuwenhoek (1632-1723)

119

(Fig. 44) was a leading advocate among another group of preformationists – the animalculists – who argued, with microscopic evidence, that the pre-formed entity preexisted in the male germ element, the sperm.

131. In contrast to preformation beliefs, some authorities argued that embryonic forms came together following a particular pattern, adding sequential structures to growing embryos piecemeal. This doctrine, called epigenesis, gained its greatest support through the influential experimental reports of William Harvey (1578 - 1657), published as *Exercitations de Generatione Animalium* (London: O. Pulleyn, 1651). Accounting for the role of both female and male contributions, Harvey argued that all animals are derived from a "primordium" or ovum produced by the female and having the innate capacity to develop after receiving the influence of the male semen.

132. Lorenzo Magalotti (1637-1712), secretary to the Accademia del Cimento in Florence, demonstrated some of the "natural experiments" which had been performed by members of the Accademia, to the Royal Society in London in March 1668. Richard Waller translated Magalotti's account of the experiments and the equipment used in *Essayes of Natural Experiments* (London: Alsop, 1684).

133. Serpent of Eve, Genesis Ch 7, vv 1-5, Balaam's ass, Numbers Ch 22, vv 28-30.

134. Epictetus (55-135 AD), the key Greek Stoic philosopher, compiled in *Enchiridion*, a digest of his *Discourses*, the detailed philosophical requirements for leading a calm and disciplined life. Above all, he argued, one will not fail to be happy if he desires that things should just be as they are. Such an appreciation comes from balancing what one can change with that which lies beyond the possibility of change. Simplicius (*c.*490-560 AD), a mathematician, prepared an important *Commentary* supportive of the harmony that Epictetus demonstrated between Aristotelian philosophy and that of Platonism. George Stanhope, the Dean of Canterbury, translated these arguments from the Greek in *Epictetus, His Morals, with Simplicius, His Comment* (London: R. Sare and J. Hindmarsh, 1694).

Glossary

The composite definitions offered convey, when possible, contemporary meanings and interpretations of words and phrases used in Floyer's day. Sources consulted include: Stephen Blancard *The Physical Dictionary*, 4th edition (London: S. Crouch and J. Sprint, 1702); John Quincy, *Lexicon Physico-Medicum; or, A New Medicinal Dictionary*, 5th edition (London: T. Longman, 1736); Daniel Turner, *Tabula Ætiologica* in *The Art of Surgery*, Vol. II, 6th edition (London: C. Rivington and J. Clarke, 1742); Robert James, *A Medicinal Dictionary* (London: T. Osborne and J Roberts, 1743); J. Barrow, *Dictionarium Medicum Universale; or, A New Medicinal Dictionary* (London: T. Longman and C. Hitch, 1749); Joannes Groenvelt, *The Rudiments of Physick* (Sherborne: R. Goadby and London: W. Owen, [1753]), N. Culpeper, *The English Physician Enlarged* (London: J. Barker, n.d.); Samuel Johnson, *A Dictionary of the English Language*, 10th edition (London: F. and C. Rivington, and 53 others, 1810); Robert Hooper, *Lexicon Medicum; or Medical Dictionary*, (New York: Harper & Brothers, 1845); *OED* online at <dictionary.oed.com>, 2nd edition, 1989.

Absorbents
Medicines named for their power of imbibing the sharp particles and tempering the four juices of the blood *ex absorbeo*.

Acids
All liquors and substances which affect the taste in a sharp and piercing manner. The common way of discerning whether any particular liquor or substance has particles of this kind in it is mixing it with syrup of violets which it will turn a red colour.

Acid Spirits
Those of vitriol, sulphur, &c. so called because they are specifically heavier than water and are nothing else but sharp salts divided and fused in phlegm.

Acidulae
Medicinal springs impregnated with sharp particles, as are the nitrous, chalybeate, and alum springs.

Acrid
Sharp and pungent in imitation of an acid; bitter, hot or stinging to the taste.

Acrimony
Expresses a quality in bodies by which they corrode, destroy or dissolve others.

Acupuncture
Pricking with a needle, which is much practised in Oriental nations.

Adust
Signifies humours that by long heat become hot and fiery in nature, such as choler and the like.

Adustion
Scorched by violent heat, or burnt; figuratively of the bile or choler.

Adventitious
Not natural, but springing from external causes.

Aether
A fine, fluid, subtle substance, or medium that pervades the pores of all bodies.

Aerial Spirits
Existing or moving in the atmosphere, above the earth, flying or floating in the air.

Agaric
A fungus, one form of which was renowned as a cathartic.

Agues
Intermittent fevers of all kinds.

Air
That fluid which we breathe, that is compressible, dilatable, and covers the earth to a great height; and differs from aether in refracting the rays of the heavenly luminaries.

Air-pump
An engine contrived to exhaust or draw out the air from vessels in which any living bodies or other substances may be included, to show the effects thereof.

Alcali (Alkali)
All such bodies as will ferment with acids; but more properly refers only to such salts as are made by incineration and are sometimes called lixiviate or fixed salts. The fixed salts of plants are first burnt to ashes, then made into a lixivium; but is now generally understood of all other remedies, fitted by their texture to break, blunt or sheath the specula or points of acid.

Alexipharmic
A counter-poison of any kind, relating chiefly to remedies in malignant fevers.

Aloetica
Medicines which chiefly consist of aloes.

Alteratives (or altering medicines)
Are such medicines as only change the qualities of the body and its humours, by heating, cooling, moistening, and drying. They are opposed to those medicines that cause vomiting, purging, sweating, and transpiration.

Alum/Alumen
A genus of earthy salt, it consists of the vitriolic acid and a clayey earth.

Amulet
An ornament, gem, scroll, or a package containing a relic worn as a charm or preservative against evils or mischief, such as diseases and witchcraft, and generally inscribed with mystic forms or characters.

Analysis
Reducing by chemistry any matter into its primary constituent or compounding parts.

Anasarca
A watery swelling from a serous humour shed between the skin and flesh.

Angina
Although later characterized as sudden severe pain in the chest, in the seventeenth century, it was a synonym for quinsy or sore throat.

Animal Faculties
The powers of hearing, seeing, smelling, tasting, feeling; of imagination, understanding, memory, will, going, standing, and all voluntary motion.

Animal Humours
All the juices contained in canals or vessels, and which are distinguished from one another by some manifest qualities, as healthful, vitiated, sanguine, or choleric, according to their different consistencies and principles.

Animal Secretion
Is that separation of juices from one another which is performed by the glands.

Animal Spirits (Nervous Fluid)
Consist of the smallest particles in the blood, as the result of the minuteness of their secreting glands.

Animalculum
Small living creatures not discerned by the naked eye, but which are to be discovered in many fluids by the assistance of proper glasses.

Antihecticum
A medicine for a hectic fever.

Antiscorbutic
A remedy for scurvy.

Antonius [Musa]
Roman physician who cured his patient, Augustus Caesar, by using cold bathing.

Aphthae
Specks, pimples or small ulcers about the internal parts of the mouth.

Apoplexy
An almost instantaneous deprivation of all sensation and of all voluntary motion.

Aquae acidulae
Spa waters, like those of Epsom, Barnet and Tunbridge.

Arcanum
A secret and therefore 'tis a term ridiculously applied by quacks and impostors in medicine, who generally conceal their ignorance and fraud under a pretence of secrecy.

Archeus
The highest, exalted and invisible spirit, which is separated from bodies; a hidden virtue of nature common to all things; a sort of *primum mobile* or semi deity to superintend the animal fabric or oeconomy, and to direct everything in the best manner for conservation.

Aromatic Styptics
Fragrant styptics prevented from putrefaction, especially that promoted by heat.

Aromatics
Fragrant plants or drugs.

Asthma
A frequent respiration, joined with a hissing sound and a cough, especially in the night time; caused by a sharp and scorbutic blood, which excessively vellicates the organs of respiration and puts them into a more convulsive motion, whereby the lungs are puffed up and the circulation of the blood is hindered; whence suffocation, swoons and coughs easily proceed.

Asthmatical
Troubled with shortness of breath.

Astringents
Medicines that bind together and straighten the pores and passages of the body.

Atom
Such a small particle as cannot be physically divided; and these are the first rudiments or component parts of all bodies.

Atrabilis
A degeneracy of the bile, into what the ancients called black choler.

Attentuation
Making a body or fluid thinner.

Balnea aqua dulcis
An herbal-sweetened water bath.

Bezoar Stone
Stones of a round and oval figure found in the maw or stomach of particular animals, especially ruminants. These stones were believed to act as a universal antidote against poisons.

Bile
Used to sheathe or blunt the acids of the chyle because they are entangled with its sulphurs, thickening it so that it cannot be sufficiently diluted by the succus pancreaticus to enter the lacteal vessels.

Bitters
A liquor, generally spirituous, in which a bitter herb, leaf, or root has been steeped.

Blisters
A vesicatory or plaster of Spanish Flies (*Cantharis vesicatoria*) applied to the skin to raise a blister.

Brute
An animal, without the ability to reason as it lacks the rational soul.

Cacochymical
Abounding with evil humours.

Cacochymy (Cacochymia)
A vitiated state of the humours of the body, especially of the blood.

Cataplasm
A topically applied medication, usually a poultice.

Catarrh
A defluxion or distillation of humours from the brain into any part of the body, especially the lungs, causing coughs.

Cautery
Is either actual or potential: the first is burning by a hot iron, and the latter with caustic medicines. The actual cautery is generally used to stop mortification, by burning of the dead parts to the quick, or to stop the effusion of blood by searing up the vessels.

Cephalic
Pertaining to the head.

Cerebrum
Part of the brain in which the cortical part is always on the outside, which Malpighi says is nothing but a heap of little oval glands which receive the capillary branches of the veins and arteries which belong to the brain, and which send out an infinite number of fibres which all together make up the inner medullary substance from which the nervous juice is derived into the nerves and fibres of the whole body.

126

Chalebeate (or Chalybeate)
Mineral water or spring impregnated with iron salts.

Chirurgeon (Surgeon)
One who cures ailments, not by internal medicines, but by outward applications.

Chirurgery (Surgery)
The art of a chirurgeon or surgeon, so called because of its great dependence upon manual operation and a peculiar dexterity therein; the art of curing by external application.

Choler (Bile)
One of the four humours supposed to cause irascibility of temper.

Chyle (Chylus)
A liquor like a posset into which all foods are changed in the stomach, if the digestion be good; the white milky fluid formed by the action of pancreatic juice and the bile on chyme that is contained in the lacteals.

Chymistry (or Chemistry)
That art whereby sensible bodies contained in vessels, or capable of being contained therein, are so changed by means of certain instruments, and principally fire, that their several powers and virtues are thereby discovered.

Cicatricula
That little whitish speck in the coat of the yolk of an egg in which the first changes appear towards the formation of the chick; 'tis commonly called the treddle.

Coction
In a medicinal sense, that alteration in the crude matter of a distemper whereby it is either fitted for a discharge or rendered harmless in the body. This is often brought about by nature, that is by *vis viae*, or the disposition of natural tendency of the matter itself, or else by proper remedies, which may so alter its bulk, figure, cohesion, or give it a particular determination, so as to prevent any further ill effects or drive it quite out of the body.

Coction of humours
Their being separated from the mass of good blood and fitted for expulsion.

Coeliac passion
A diarrhoea or a flux that arises from the indigestion or putrefaction of food in the stomach and bowels whereby the aliment comes away little altered from what it was when eaten or changed like corrupted stinking flesh.

Colatura
Any strained or filtered liquor.

Colia
A mackerel-like fish, difficult to digest, but used medically to promote fermentation; a resolutive.

Colic
Any disorder of the stomach or bowels in general that is attended with pain.

Colliquamentum
The first rudiments of an embryo in generation.

Colliquation
The melting of anything by heat; a dissolving or wasting of the parts.

Colliquative fever
One attended with diarrhoea or profuse sweats, from too lax a contexture of the fluids.

Congeries
A collection or parcel of bodies gathered together into one mass or com-position.

Conglobate Gland
A round gland subsisting by itself, including the glands of the mesentery and all others which receive and carry off lympha.

Conglomerate gland
That which consists of various glands, as the pancreas and saliva glands, and that has a proper excretory duct.

Consumption
A defect of nourishment or decaying of the body, particularly by a waste of muscular flesh. It is frequently attended with a hectic fever and is divided by physicians into several kinds according to the variety of causes, which must carefully be regarded in order to cure.

Convulsids
Medicines administered to contradict or cure convulsions; spasmodics.

Corporeal Machine
Iatromechanical medical term for the human body.

Cortical Glands (Glandulous Cortex)
The outer substance of the brain.

Coryza (or Gravedo)
A defluxion of a sharp salt and thickened humour into the mouth, lungs and nostrils, from the ventricles of the brain, by the nerves of smelling. For when it grows thick, it can neither be percolated by the reins, nor pass from the pituitary gland, through the infundibulum into the veins, and therefore it distils into the nostrils by the aforesaid nerves, which if it meet with sulphurous particles, it produces a fever and consequently thirst.

Crasis (Temperamentum)
A convenient mixture of qualities; temperament is either simple or compound, simple when only one quality exceeds the rest, as hot, cold, moist, dry, salt and sharp, acid and frigid, acid and acrimonious, and also when one is inherent which is fixed in the parts. It is such a due mixture of qualities in a human body as constitutes a state of health.

Crisis
The termination of a disease, either by death or recovery.

Critical day or day of judgement
That day in fevers especially wherein it appears on which side sentence is given, whether on the plaintiff's, viz. the disease; or on nature's, the defendant; so that by some evacuation or swelling or other great mutation to the better or worse, it appears whether the patient is like to recover or not.

Crude
Raw, undigested, or meat not well digested or roasted crudely, and blood and other humours not well digested by the stomach and liver.

Crudities
Rawness; indigestion.

Cupping
Application of a cupping glass, either hot or cold, to draw forth the blood, a humour, to a precise bodily location.

Datura
A genus of plants of which thorn-apple or strammony is a powerful narcotic and occasions madness.

Defluxion
The same as distillation; also a running together of humours into any part causing pain or swelling.

Deist
One who acknowledges the existence of God, but without any other article of religious faith.

Deliquium
Swooning away.

Delirium
Raving or talking idly, especially in time of sickness.

Deobstruent
A medicine which removes obstructions; an aperient.

Depuration
The freeing of any liquor or solid body from its foulness.

Diaphoretic
A medicine or agent which promotes perspiration. Diaphoretics differ from sudorifics: the former only increase the insensible perspiration, the latter excite the sensible discharge called sweat.

Dispensatory
A book in which medicinal substances, their composition, method of preparation and use are described.

Distemper
Any excess of the four qualities, heat, cold, moisture, dryness. There are reckoned four simple or single distempers, viz. a hot, a cold, a moist, a dry, and four compounds, viz. hot and moist, hot and dry, cold and moist, cold and dry.

Dropsy (Hydrops)
Water is the most visible cause of the distemper, derived from too lax a tone of the solids, whereby digestion is weakened and all the body parts stuffed beyond measure. The cure consists in evacuation and strengthening the fibres of the whole body.

Dura menix
The outer, thickest layer of the meninges, surrounding the brain and spinal cord.

Dyscrasia (Dyscrasy)
Intemperature. Such a mixture of fluids in the body as is inconsistent with health.

Dysenteries
A painful discharge from the bowels by stool, often called the bloody flux.

Earth
One of the chymical principles: that part of bodies called *caput mortuum* that is last in the furnace and is neither capable of being raised by distillation nor dissolved by solution.

Ebullition
Working of the blood in the veins.

Economy (Animal Œconomy)
Strictly the management of family concerns, but in figurative sense, enlarged to the mechanism and function of a human body, such that animal oeconomy includes all that concerns the human structure in a state of health.

Effervescence
Expresses a greater degree of motion or struggling of the small parts of a liquor than is commonly understood by fermentation or ebullition; a state which occasions great heat.

Electuaries
Medicines made up of conserves of herbs, to which is added some sweet spicy powder and so with syrup is prepared in the form of treacle.

Element
Known since the pre-Socratic Greeks as the four primary substances: air, earth, fire and water.

Emollient
Such things as sheath and soften the asperities of the humours, and relax and supple the solids at the same time. Emollients lubricate and moisten the fibres so as to relax them into their proper dimensions, whereupon such disorders cease.

Empiric

A tryer or experimenter, but regularly signifies those persons who have no true education in or knowledge of the grounds of physical practice, but venture upon hear-say and observation only. Medicine was almost altogether in the hands of empirics before Hippocrates and many pretended only to one disease, which they had accustomed themselves to; but the Prince of Physic added reason thereunto and taught the advantages of theory. Latter ages are again much degenerated into empiricism and for every one regular physician, such is the defect of our laws at present in this respect, there are fifty that practise at present that are empirics.

Emulgent arteries and veins

Bring the wheyish excrement of the blood into the kidneys, where it becomes urine and is passed by the ureters into the bladder.

Emulsions

Medicines resembling milk, generally made from farinaceous seeds and beat up with some fluid by which their oily parts are intimately blended with it.

Ephemera

A continued fever which lasts but a day, arising from a commotion and ascension of the fire parts of the blood.

Epidemical Fevers

Those which spread rapidly, attacking many persons at the same time as they spread.

Epiphora

An inflammation caused by a defluxion of humours upon the eyes.

Evacuation

Signifies any diminution of the animal fluids by cathartics, blood letting, or other means.

Excrementitious

Of or belonging to excrements; impure preternatural humours; any humour thrown forth from the body as useless such as urine, stool &c., in contradistinction to those that are nutritious.

Explosion

The going off of gun-powder and the report made thereby; but also used frequently to express such hidden actions of bodies as have some resemblance thereto, as those which ferment with violence immediately upon their mixture and occasion a cracking sound. Some writers have likewise applied it to the excursions of animal spirits and instantaneous motions of the fibres on the mind's direction.

Extemporaneous form
A prescription containing several ingredients made up by an apothecary, usually on the instruction of a physician for a particular occasion; by contrast, a simple was a single ingredient in a medicine or, popularly, a herb.

Extravasation
A discharge or escape, as of blood, from a vessel into the tissues, such as ecchymosis, bruising or aneurism.

Fasiculus
The outer covering of a body of nerve fibres.

Fermentation
The working of humours as new drink works in the barrel. Fermentation is an intestine motion amongst the heterogeneous parts of any body, by which it is by some means agitated and grows full of air.

Fever
An augmented velocity of the blood. The almost infinite variety of causes of this distemper does so diversify its appearances and indicate so many ways of cure that our room here will not allow of any more than to refer to Bellini and Cheyne for the theory, and Riverius, Willis, Sydenham and Morton for the practice.

Fibre
A fibre, in physic, is an animal thread of which some are soft, flexible and a little elastic; and these are either hollow, like small pipes, or spongeous and full of little cells, as the nervous and fleshy fibres. Others are more solid, flexible, and with a strong elasticity or spring, as the membranous and cartilaginous fibres; and a third sort is hard and flexible, as the fibres of the bones. Some are so very small as not to be easily perceived, and others which are plainly seen are composed of still smaller fibres.

Fibrilla
A minute thread of fibre, as one of the fibrous elements of a muscle.

Fluor albus
The whites or a vaginal discharge of white, mucous, fluid matter.

133

Fluxes
Abnormally copious flowing of blood or excrement from the bowels or other organs; a morbid or excessive discharge; a flowing out, issue or discharge of humours.

Foetids
Pills containing asafoetida, a gum resin from the Middle East.

Foetor
An offensive smell or stench.

Fomentation
When linen cloths or sponges are dipped in some hot liquor and applied to the diseased part.

Frictions
Used by physicians for rubbing any bodily part to dislodge any obstructed humours or promote a due motion of the included juices. This is of great service in several distempers, especially those that proceed from a stoppage of insensible perspiration or an obstruction of the skin pores.

Fusion
The conversion of metals into fluids, or more generally, the melting of anything.

Galenical
Medicine founded upon the principles of Galen which consists chiefly in multiplying herbs and roots in the same composition, as opposed to chymical medicines.

Gentian
A plant which resists putrefaction, poison, and prevents the pestilence; it strengthens the stomach exceedingly, helps digestion, comforts the heart, and preserves it against fainting and swooning.

Glandulous Cortex (Cortical Glands)
The outer substance of the brain.

Globuli (Globules)
Small particles of matter of a globular or spherical figure, as the red particles of the blood.

Gout
A disease which may affect any membranous part but commonly those which are at the greatest distance from the heart or the brain, especially

the great toe, where the motion of the fluids is the slowest, the resistance, friction and structure of the solid parts the greatest, and the sensation of pain by the dilacerations of nervous fibres, extreme.

Gravedo (See Coryza)

Gum
A concreted vegetable juice which flows through the bark of certain trees and hardens upon the surface. It differs from a resin in being more viscid and less friable and generally dissolving in water; whereas a resin, by being more sulphurous, requires a spiritous menstruum.

Gum Ammoniacum
A gum much used in physic, so called because the plant which produced it was supposed to grow about the temple of Jupiter Ammon in Libya.

Gum Guaicum
This tree producing this gum grows in Jamaica and other parts of the West Indies. The gum is very hot and drying, and therefore a great promoter of insensible perspiration, rather than sweat. It is reckoned a wonderful sweetener and cleanser of the blood, and therefore much prescribed in cutaneous foulness of all kinds. By the same hot penetrating quality, it is also esteemed good in the gout, by dissipating and insensibly wasting the humours thrown upon the joints; as, likewise in dropsies and catarrhs, by drying up and wasting the superfluous humidities. In venereal diseases it does wonders and thus is called pock-wood.

Gutta Serena
Dimness of sight.

Hectic
A fever which accompanies consumption or other wasting diseases and is attended with flushed cheeks and a hot dry skin.

Hellborne (Hellebore)
Plant used medically since the Ancients, particularly helpful for opening uterine obstructions and promoting menstruation.

Haemoptysis (Haemoptoe)
Spitting of blood, expectoration of blood or of bloody mucus from the lungs or bronchi.

Henbane
Its leaves cool all hot inflammations and are good to assuage all manner of swellings; it also assuages the pain of the gout, the sciatica and other

pains in the joints and helps the headache and want of sleep in hot fevers; the oil of the seed is helpful for deafness. This herb must never be taken inwardly.

Hermetica
That which is directed by chymical reasonings upon the principles of salt, sulphur and mercury.

Hermetical Physicians
Chymists such as trade with furnaces, pots and glasses to draw spirits, oils and waters, to make salts and quintessences; called so from Hermes Trismegistus, an Egyptian philosopher who is thought to have been an alchemist.

Horror
A vibration or trembling of the skin over the whole body, with chills after it; shaking with cold is common in the first attack of all fevers, but particularly in the intermitting fevers or agues.

Humour
All the juices contained in an animal body's canals or vessels which are distinguished from one another by some manifest qualities as healthful, vitiated, sanguine, or choleric, according to their different consistencies and principles.

Hydatid
A membranous sac or bladder filled with a pellucid fluid found in various parts of the bodies of animals, but unconnected with the tissues.

Hypochondria
The parts of the body beneath the ribs or under the cartilages of the chest.

Hypochondriac
Melancholy; disordered in the imagination. The blood moving too slowly through the coeliac and mesenteric arteries produces various complaints in the lower bowels and hypochondres, from whence such persons are called hypochondriacs.

Hypochondriacus affectus
A purely flatulent and convulsive passion arising from flatulent and pungent humours in the spleen or sweet-bread, which afflicts the nervous and membranous parts.

Hysterical Affections
Disorders of the womb that bring the whole nervous system frequently into disorder, the sufferer of this disorder being termed an hysteric.

Iliac passion
Is a kind of nervous colic whose seat is the ileum, whereby the gut is twisted or one part enters the cavity of the part immediately above or below.

Iliosa
Abdominal colic brought about by a twisting of the gut.

Imagination
That faculty by which we, as it were, picture corporeal substances in the mind, as if we saw them actually with our eyes.

Imposthume
A collection of matter or pus in any part, either from an obstruction of fluids in that part which makes them change into such matter, or from a translation of it into some part other than where it is generated.

Incide
Medicines which consist of pointed and sharp particles such as acids and most salts, by which the particles of other bodies are divided from one another; thus expectorating medicines are to incide or cut the phlegm.

Incogitancy
Want of the faculty of thought.

Incrassating
The rendering of fluids thicker than before.

Incumbent Air
The atmospheric air pressing down upon the body.

Indication
One of four kinds: 1. Prophylactic or preservatory, which relates to the preservation of health by the adverting of diseases. 2. Curatory, which relates to the removal of diseases. 3. Vital, which relates to the immediate preservation of life. 4. Urgent, mitigatory or palliative, which relates to the mitigation of the symptoms when too violent to be neglected, till the determination of the disease.

Inflammation
When the blood is obstructed so as to crowd in a greater quantity into any particular part, and give it a greater colour and heat than normal.

Inflation
A blowing up; the stretching or filling any part with a flatulent or windy substance.

Inoculation
The ingrafting of one tree upon another. This term of late has also been used for the practice of transplanting the small-pox, by infusion of matter from ripened pustules into the veins of the uninfected, in hopes of procuring a milder sort than what frequently comes by infection.

Insensible
Not perceived by the outward senses of seeing, hearing, smelling, touching or tasting.

Intemperies (Dyscrasy)
Any disorder or indisposition of the blood or humours.

Intermittent pulse
That which holds up a while and then beats again and then stops and then beats again. This is a sign of great sickness.

Ischuria
A stoppage of urine whether by stone, gravel or any other cause.

Lacteals (Lacteal Veins)
Passing from the intestines, circulating a milk-white fluid. Lacteal veins are long and slender pipes, whose coats are so thin as to become invisible when they are not distended with chyle or lymph. They arise from all the parts of the small guts by fine capillary tubes, which as they run from the sides of the guts to the glands in the mesentery, unite and form larger branches.

Languor
To grow faint; a weakness or sickness of the spirits.

Laxity of a fibre
The degree of cohesion in its parts which a small force can alter so as to increase its length beyond what is natural, and therefore it is a species of debility.

Lethargy
A distemper where there seems to be an utter loss of all the rational powers and inaptitude to motion; a drowsiness, like another disease, causing an heavy sleep or coma accompanied with a fever and delirium. This distemper does not seem to come of itself, but rather from the denigration of fevers.

Lientery
A particular looseness or diarrhoea wherein the food passes so suddenly through the stomach and guts as to be thrown out by stool with little or no alteration.

Liquor
Anything liquid; commonly used for fluids inebriating, or impregnated by something, or made by decoction.

Lixivium (Lixivial salt)
A liquor made by the infusion of ashes or any burnt substances, which is more or less pungent and penetrating as it is impregnated with salts and fiery particles abounding therein. That which is left after the evaporation of such a liquor is called a lixivial or lixiviate salt.

Luxation
Complete dislocation of a joint.

Macula
A spot, a blemish or cutaneous efflorescence which changes the colour of the skin.

Masticatory
A medicinal substance to be chewed.

Methodica
That practice which was conducted by rules such as were taught by Galen and his followers, in opposition to the empirical practice.

Mola (*Mola convulsiva uteri*)
A fleshy mass or formless concretion of extravasted blood or glandulous flesh in the womb generally called a false conception, which may bring about convulsions.

Morbific
Matter causing diseases; the disease is cured by the critical resolution, concoction and evacuation of the morbific matter.

Morion (Murrain)
Cattle plague.

Mucilagenous
Containing, secreting, or coated with mucilage or other viscid substance.

Mucus
That which flows from the papillary processes through the *os cribriforme* into the nostrils; also any slimy liquor or moisture, as that which daubs over and guards the bowels and all the chief passages in the body.

Natural heat
A swift and confused motion of the subtle matter or of a small fire without light, such as is perceived in quick lime mixed with water and in the various fermentations of the chymists, in horse-dung, and in herbs putrefying in a heap, yet hot and differing only in degree from common fire. This motion arises because the subtle matter insinuating itself into the blood and not finding a free passage must therefore exert its power upon the particles of the blood and agitate them confusedly; it proceeds from the same cause as fermentation.

Natural things (The Naturals)
They are seven, viz. the elements, the temperaments, the humours, the spirits, the parts, the faculties and the actions.

Nerve
A long and small bundle of very fine pipes or hollow fibres. The medullary substance of the brain is the beginning of all the nerves and 'tis probable that each fibre of the nerves answers to a particular part of the brain at one end and to a particular part of the body at its other end, that whenever an impression is made upon such a part of the brain the soul may know that such a part of the body is affected. The nerves ordinarily accompany the arteries through all the body so that the animal spirits may be kept warm and moving by the continual heat and pulse of the arteries.

Nervous Papillae
The immediate organ in the senses of feeling, taste and smell.

Non-Naturals
Physicians since the time of Galen reckon these to be six, viz. air, meat and drink, sleep and watching, motion and rest, retention and excretion, and the passions of the mind.

Obstructions
Blocking up of any canal in the human body so as to prevent the flowing of any fluid throughout.

Œdema
A tumour, now commonly confined by surgeons to a white insensible tumour proceeding from cold and aqueous humours.

Omentum
A free fold of the peritoneum or a fold serving to connect viscera and support blood vessels. The great omentum is a sac which is attached to the stomach and transverse colon, is loaded with fat and covers more or less of the intestines; the caul. The lesser omentum connects the stomach and liver and contains the liver's vessels.

Organical part
That part of an animal or vegetable which is designed for the performance of some particular action, in opposition to non-organical which cannot of itself perform an action.

Oscillation
To swing up and down like a see-saw, upon a rope, or a board laid across a plank. In medicine it is applied to the tonic motion of the fibres, like that of the peristaltic one of the guts.

Parotis
An inflammation or an abscess of the parotid gland.

Pathognomonic
Such signs of a disease that are inseparable, thereby telling the essence or real nature of the disease.

Pathology
That part of physic which shows the diseased constitution of the body; is that part of medicine which relates to the distempers with their differences, causes and effects, incident to the human body.

Peri-pneumonia
An inflammation of some parts of the contents of the thorax, usually of the lungs; three kinds are distinguished, the true, the spurious and the catarrhous.

Perspirable
When the individual pores or holes in the skin are kept open, so that the vapours arising from evil humours may freely breathe out.

Pestilential Fever (Pestis)
The plague; a genus of disease which is contagious in the extreme with prostration of strength, buboes, and carbuncles, petechiae, haemorrhage and colliquative diarrhoea.

Phrenitis
Inflammation of the brain or of the meninges of the brain, attended with acute fever and delirium.

Phthisis
Consumption.

Physic (Physick)
Physic is the art of preserving health, and restoring it when lost: that science by the knowledge of which life and health are preserved or, when lost, health restored. The chief end of physic is health and, next to this, the mitigation of symptoms. Present health is to be preserved by physic and, if lost, to be recovered by it; the first of these is called the hygienic part, the other the therapeutic part. The object of physic is man, that is his life, health, diseases, their causes from whence they arise, and the means by which they are governed; an art assistant to nature and preserving health in human bodies as much as is possible by convenient remedies.

Sennertus and others rightly divide Physic into five parts: 1. Physiologia which treats of human constitution as it is found, to which belongs Anatomy too. 2. Pathologia which treats of the preternatural constitution of our bodies. 3. Semiotica which treats of the signs of health and diseases. 4. Hygiena which delivers rules of the regimen to be observed in the preservation of health. 5. Therapeutica which teaches Diet, Chyrurgery, and Medicine. Hippocrates calls it a long art and Paracelsus a short one and certain Arabians a little one, but in reality it is a long, great and noble art.

Physician
One highly skilled in the art of physic, modest, sober and courteous. The sixteenth-century physician, Julius Caesar Scaliger describes a physician thus: he ought to be learned, honest, mild, and diligent, a fortunate man and of ripe years, one that relies upon God, not arrogant with his knowledge, labour or success, nor covetous.

Physiologia
That part of physic which teaches the natural constitution of the human body.

142

Phytologia
The knowledge or description of vegetables and plants.

Pituita (Phlegm)
The most viscid and glutinous part of the blood which is separated in the largest glands where the arteries are largest and give the greatest retardation to the blood's velocity, as in the glands about the mouth, head and brain.

Plethora
When there is more good blood than is requisite; it happens either to the vessels when they are stretched out and cannot hold all or sometimes, though the vessels be not over full, their strength is over-loaded.

Pleurisy
A disease characterized by pain in the chest or side, fever, loss of appetite, usually caused by chill.

Pleuritis
An inflammation of the membrane, pleura and the intercostal muscles, attended with a continual fever and stitches in the side, difficulty of breathing and sometimes spitting blood.

Pneuma
Air or an all-pervading fiery essence in the air which was the creative and animating spirit of the universe; drawn into the body through the lungs, it generated and sustained the innate heat in the left ventricle of the heart and was distributed by the arteries to the brain and all parts of the body.

Polypus
A tumour, usually with a narrow base, somewhat resembling a pear, found in the nose, uterus, &c. and produced by hypertrophy of some portion of the mucous membrane.

Pores
Little holes in the skin through which vapours and sweat come out; sometimes they are visible upon the arm or leg being swelled and closed with cold, resembling a goose skin for roughness.

Porta
The part of the liver or other organ where its vessels and nerves enter.

Posca
A mixture of vinegar with water.

Poultice
A soft composition, as of bread, bran or a mucilaginous substance, to be applied to sores or inflamed parts of the body; a cataplasm.

Preternatural
Beyond the intent or custom of nature.

Prisca Medicina
Ancient medicine.

Prognosis and Prognostic Signs
Signs by which we know the event of a disease, whether it shall end in life or death or be long or short; a foretelling of the issue or event of a disease founded upon a right knowledge of its nature and common or customary way of its termination.

Psychrolusia
The cold bath or washing in cold water, much used by the ancients to restore the tone of the parts after warm bathing, to give a firmness to the body.

Punctum Saliens
That speck in the egg which is called the treddle and is first to have motion in the formation of the chick.

Puncture
Any wound made by a pointed instrument.

Pyretologia
A discourse upon or description of fevers.

Quality
The properties or affections of any being whereby it acquires some particular denomination. Those which are cognizable by the senses in terms of figure, solidity, &c. are called sensible qualities.

Quartan
A cyclic fever in which seventy-two hours elapse between attacks.

Quinsy
An inflammation of the throat or parts adjacent, especially of the fauces or tonsils, attended by considerable swelling, painful and impeded deglutition and accompanied by inflammatory fever; it sometimes creates danger of suffocation.

Rarefied Air
Air which is made less dense usually by heating, as in cupping.

Raucedo
Hoarseness.

Regimen
In a medical sense, meaning the due ordering or government of sick people.

Rickets
A distemper in children from an unequal distribution of nourishment whereby the joints grow knotty and the limbs uneven; its cure is performed by evacuation and friction.

Sal Ammonia
The compound of the muriatic acid, or acid of sea-salt, and the volatile alkali.

Sal Jovis (Salt of Jupiter, Tin)
It is made by dissolving the magistry of Jupiter by digesting it in spirit of wine vinegar, filtrating and coagulating. It is a remedy against suffocation of the womb or fits of the mother which it helps in a miraculous manner, being both inwardly taken and outwardly applied.

Scarification
An incision of the skin with a lancet or such-like instrument and is most practised in cupping, which acts by stimulation as well as by evacuation.

Sceptic
One who doubted the truth of anything till thoroughly examined, though some go so far under this pretence as hardly to be convinced by any evidences. Galen makes mention in his time of a public school or college of physicians who professed themselves sceptic; but Cartesius has of late given much encouragement to this sect, whom he hath taught to call everything in question till re-examined; and our countryman Mr Boyle hath wrote a book well known under the title of *The Sceptical Chymist*, where everything is laid down by way of enquiry rather than as matter well known and settled.

Schirrhus
A hard swelling without pain.

Scrobiculum Cordis
The pit of the stomach, the word scrobiculum standing for a little pit or furrow.

Scrofula
A constitutional disease thought to be hereditary, especially manifested by chronic enlargement and cheesy degeneration of the lymphatic glands particularly those of the neck, and marked by a tendency to the development of chronic intractable inflammations of the skin, mucous membrane, bones, joints and other parts and by a diminution in the power of resistance to disease or injury.

Scurvy
A constitution wherein the blood is unequally fluid, and is best remedied by stimuli, exercise, and such means as assist in sanguification.

Secerned
The liquor or juice separated or secreted by the glands.

Secession
The going off by secretion, as the excrements are particularly said to be formed by the secession of those parts, whereof they consist, from the animal fluids, through their proper outlets.

Sensible Soul
The soul common to all organisms, beyond which the animals are endowed with an animal soul and humans with a rational soul.

Serum
The thin part of the blood.

Seton
A hole made in the skin and a skein of silk or yarn drawn through and kept in, which being removed daily, causes the matter and humour to come away.

Simples
Medicines unmixed and uncompounded.

Sinapism
A cataplasm made chiefly of mustard.

Siziness
Viscidness.

Sizy
Resembling size, thick, viscous and glutinous.

Sordes
The putrid filth lying undigested in some wounds and rotten ulcers, being
thick and sticking fast therein.

Soul
The immaterial and immortal spirit of man.

Specific Medicines
Those medicines which have a peculiar virtue against one disease.

Specific quality
A peculiar hidden property, not springing from the first qualities.

Spirit
The animating or vital principle in man and animals which gives life to
the physical organism, in contrast to its purely material elements; the
breath of life.

Spirits
Spirits are reckoned of three sorts, the animal spirits in the brain, the vital
spirits in the heart and the natural spirits in the liver. Seventeenth-Century
authors distinguish them only into two kinds, the animal in the brain and
the vital and natural (which are accounted the same) in the blood. The
animal spirits are a very thin liquor which, distilling from the blood in the
outward or cortical substance of the brain, is exalted into spirits and thence
through the medullar substance of the brain are derived into the nerves
and spinal marrow and, in them performed, all the actions of sense and
motion. The vital or natural spirits are the subtlest parts of the blood,
which actuate and ferment it and make it fit for nourishment.

Steel (Chalybeate Medicine)
Iron as used medicinally.

Sternutatories
Medicines procuring sneezing.

Stramonium
Thorny-apple or stink-weed, a species of *Datura*.

Styptic
Signifies anything that binds together. Astringents, generally those which
are applied to stop haemorrhages.

147

Sudoric
Pertaining to sweat; sudoric acids are present in human sweat.

Sudorifics
Medicines promoting sweat.

Sulphur
Brimstone; it is considered a principle by chymists.

Superficies
The outside or surface of anything, without any dimension or thickness.

Suppuration
A collection of matter in an imposthume; the ripening or change of matter of a tumour into pus, which may be effected either by natural means by *vis vitae* or by the use of artificial compositions, such as plaisters or cataplasms.

Sympathy
Fellow-feeling; a disease is said to come by sympathy when the principal cause is in some other part with which the part offended hath a fellow feeling; so pains in the head caused by evil humours in the stomach are said to come by sympathy, and sickness of the stomach caused by the stone in the kidneys is a disease of the stomach by sympathy.

Sympathetic Powders
A reputed remedy brought about by applying medicine to the weapon that inflicted a wound.

Tabes
A consumption of the body; a marasmus.

Tartar
A hard substance found sticking to wine casks from which the chymists prepare many medicines; it is highly serviceable for gently cleansing the first passages, in a small dose, or for purging strongly in a larger quantity.

Taste
Expresses that sensation which all things taken into the mouth give particularly to the tongue, the papillae of which are the principal instruments.

Temperament (Temperies)
That diversity in the blood of different persons whereby it is more apt to fall into some certain combinations in one body than another, whether

into choler, phlegm, etc. from whence persons are said to be of a bilious or phlegmatic temperament, or the like. A temper or mean as to heat, cold, etc. in such temperament; a well constituted habit of body.

Tenesmus
Straining, especially ineffectual and painful straining at stool or in urination.

Terebration
A surgical perforation through the ribs, used to relieve dropsy of the breast; any instrumental perforation of the bones as well as the head.

Terra Japonica
The learned are not agreed about this exotic drug; some who take it for a true and genuine species of earth as its name imports, rank it among minerals, others believe it to be a compound substance participating of a vitriolic nature, and others reckon it in the class of vegetable substances and take it for an inspissated juice. It is an astringent that corroborates the stomach, removes a nausea, excites the appetite, represses vomiting and stops fluxes of the belly, of the menses, and haemorrhages.

Terrestrial Particles (See Earth)

Tertian
An intermittent fever, which returns every third day reckoning inclusively or, in which, the intermission lasts one day.

Tincture
Any liquor saturated with ingredients of any kind.

Torpor
A numbness caused by deficient sensation.

Toxic
The effect produced by any venom or poison.

Tympanitis
Inflammation of the lining membrane of the middle ear.

Unction
The action of anointing or rubbing with ointment or oil.

Ustion
The action of burning; cauterisation.

Vapours
Steams ascending into the head, like the steams we see mounting from a mess of hot broth or meat.

Vigilia
Watching; a state of wakefulness or inability to sleep.

Vis Vitae
The joint action of all the parts of a human body whereby the machine is continually recruited and put in order; but, when anything proves too hard to be conquered by this, such as when a disease ensues, nature is over-burdened and, if it cannot be lessened or thrown off, the disease either proves mortal or becomes incurable.

Vital function
Faculty of the heart causing life, pulse-beating and breathing.

Vitriolic Acid
Sulphuric acid.

Vomica
A suppurated impostume or abscess with a suppuration; an encysted tumour in the lungs.

Vomitories
Medicines that cause or induce vomiting; an emetic.

Wormwood
The plant *Artemisia absinthium*, proverbial for its bitter taste; the leaves and tops are used as a tonic and vermifuge.

Index of Names and Places